Principles of Biomacromolecular Mass Spectrometry

PRINCIPLES OF BIOMACROMOLECULAR MASS SPECTROMETRY

SIMONE KOENIG
EDITOR

Nova Science Publishers, Inc.
New York

For permission to use material from this book please contact us:
Telephone 631-231-7269; Fax 631-231-8175
Web Site: http://www.novapublishers.com

LIBRARY OF CONGRESS CATALOGING-IN-PUBLICATION DATA

Principles of biomacromolecular mass spectrometry / Simone Koenig (editor).
p. cm.
Includes bibliographical references and index.
ISBN 1-60021-063-5
1. Mass spectrometry. 2. Biomolecules--Analysis. I. Koenig, Simone.
QP519.9.M3P75 2006
572'.36--dc22 2006004659

Published by Nova Science Publishers, Inc. ✣ New York

Contents

PREFACE

Mass spectrometry has proven its applicability to the measurement of almost any molecule. However, different substances require special knowledge in the respective field and scientists tend to focus on their particular task in collaborations and meetings. Nevertheless, disciplines have become more and more interdisciplinary and scientists now have to acquire knowledge in many scientific fields other than our own. Especially mass spectrometrists who often find themselves learning about the history of their sample, be it from a zoologist, clinician, microbiologist, or biochemist. This was evident with the rise of proteomics, which reaches across species and research projects, uniting scientists through the methodology. This book covers research in the fields of biomacromolecules such as proteins, DNA, and other biopolymers studied with mass spectrometry.

Structural variability resulting from protein post-translational glycosylation vastly increases the range of biological functions produced from the genome. The chemistry of glycans differs from that of proteins and dictates the use of specialized mass spectrometric techniques for successful analysis. Moreover, the unique chemistry of each glycoconjugate class drives the need for tailored analytical techniques. Glycosaminoglycans (GAGs) are linear glycans that coat the surfaces of all animal cells, bound to syndecan and glypican proteoglycan core proteins. There, they play developmentally critical roles as co-receptors for many classes of growth factors and growth factor receptors. Animal cells grow in organized extracellular matrix environments consisting of proteins, glycoproteins and proteoglycans. GAGs serve to create and support immobilized growth factor gradients and play structural roles in these extracellular matrices. Although, due to their acidity, fragility and polydispersity, GAGs have traditionally proven difficult to analyze using mass spectrometry, effective new approaches have emerged over the past few years. Chapter 1 summarizes structural biochemistry of GAGs and the uses of mass spectrometry in their analysis, with an emphasis on recent developments that have proven effective.

FTICR (Fourier transform ion cyclotron resonance) mass spectrometry offers several advantages for the analysis of biological samples, including excellent mass resolution, ultra-high mass accuracy, and a wide mass range. Chapter 2 gives a short overview of recent applications and technological developments of FTICRMS, which are relevant to the field of protein analysis. Tandem mass spectrometry, "bottom up" and "top down" approaches for protein analysis as well as methods for studying protein conformations are described and illustrated with examples.

In chapter 3, matrix assisted laser desorption ionization time-of-flight mass spectrometry (MALDI-TOF MS) and isoelectric focusing (IEF) of pure recombinant human MIA (melanoma inhibitory activity) protein, as expressed in CHO cells, indicated that part of the protein was post-translationally modified. Whereas standard positive ion mode MALDI analysis of intact MIA revealed an additional peak 80 Da higher than the theoretical mass, IEF showed three major protein bands which could all unequivocally be identified as MIA isoforms by peptide mass fingerprinting. Negative ionization MALDI mass spectrometry on a quadrupole TOF instrument indicated that the differences between these isoforms were due to one or two 80 Da modifications confined to tryptic fragment 59-76. The identity of the 80 Da post-translational modification (PTM) was determined to be a Tyr-O-sulfation through enzymatic removal of the 80 Da moiety from MIA by arylsulfatase treatment, and through the absence of the 80 Da modification(s) in MIA harvested from cells cultured in the presence of chlorate, which is known to inhibit Tyr-O-sulfation. The PTM being sulfation was further corroborated by its metastability upon MALDI-TOF MS analysis. It is concluded that the CHO produced MIA is partially post-translationally modified by Tyr-O-sulfation at positions 69 and/or 70 (^{59}LFWGGSVQGD**YY**GDLAAR^{76}). Protein Tyr-O-sulfation, has been reported to serve various functions, including modulation of protein-protein interactions. Combination of this notion with the observation that the eukaryotic MIA protein shows only a weak binding towards laminin and fibronectin leads to the speculation that the putative *in vivo* metastasis promoting activity of MIA may be based on the interaction of MIA with an as yet unknown factor via Tyr-(O)-sulfation enhanced binding kinetics.

Many prokaryotes use polyhydroxyalkanoates (PHA) as storage compounds for carbon and/or energy in the form of water-insoluble inclusion PHA granules in the cytoplasm. The surface of such granules is covered by proteins which also affect their form and structure. In chapter 4, phasin PhaP1 protein was identified in high abundance on the grana surface of *R. eutropha* employing gel electrophoretic separation and mass spectrometry. Homologous phasins PhaP3 and Pha4 were visualized using 2D-PAGE in the PhaP1 knock-out mutant, but no evidence for the presence of PhaP2 could be found. All detected phasins exhibit isoforms whose structural differences are still a matter of investigation, although C-terminally truncated isoforms of PhaP1 were detected with FTICR-MS.

The Münster Conference on Single Cell Analysis was held in Münster on November 16, 2004. Chapter 5 is an overview of topics discussed at the conference. Chapter 6 contains the speaker abstracts from the conference.

REVIEWS

In: Principles of Biomacromolecular Mass Spectrometry ISBN 1-60021-063-5
Editor: Simone Koenig, pp. 3-36

Chapter 1

PRINCIPLES OF MASS SPECTROMETRY OF GLYCOSAMINOGLYCANS

Joseph Zaia[1]
Boston University, Department of Biochemistry,
Mass Spectrometry Resource

1. ABSTRACT

Structural variability resulting from protein post-translational glycosylation vastly increases the range of biological functions produced from the genome. The chemistry of glycans differs from that of proteins and dictates the use of specialized mass spectrometric techniques for successful analysis. Moreover, the unique chemistry of each glycoconjugate class drives the need for tailored analytical techniques. Glycosaminoglycans (GAGs) are linear glycans that coat the surfaces of all animal cells, bound to syndecan and glypican proteoglycan core proteins. There, they play developmentally critical roles as co-receptors for many classes of growth factors and growth factor receptors. Animal cells grow in organized extracellular matrix environments consisting of proteins, glycoproteins and proteoglycans.
GAGs serve to create and support immobilized growth factor gradients and play structural roles in these extracellular matrices. Although, due to their acidity, fragility and polydispersity, GAGs have traditionally proven difficult to analyze using mass spectrometry, effective new approaches have emerged over the past few years. This review summarizes structural biochemistry of GAGs and the uses of mass spectrometry in their analysis, with an emphasis on recent developments that have proven effective.

2. ABBREVIATIONS

CE	capillary electrophoresis
CID	collisional-induced dissociation
CS	chondroitin sulfate
DHB	2,5-dihydroxybenzoic acid

[1] Dr. Joseph Zaia, Boston University School of Medicine, 715 Albany St., R-806, Boston, MA 02118. e-mail: jzaia@bu.edu. ph: 617-638-6762. Fax: -6761

DS	dermatan sulfate
ESI	electrospray ionization
FAB	fast atom bombardment
GAG	glycosaminoglycan
Gal	galactose
GalNAc	*N*-acetylgalactosamine
GlcA	glucuronic acid
GlcN	glucosamine
GlcNAc	*N*-acetylglucosamine
HexA	glucuronic acid or iduronic acid
ΔHexA	4,5-unsaturated uronic acid
HS	heparan sulfate
IdoA	iduronic acid
KS	keratan sulfate
MALDI	matrix-assisted laser desorption/ionization
TOF	time-of-flight
Xyl	xylose

3. INTRODUCTION

As the field of proteomics matures, researchers are coming to appreciate the complexity of mature gene products [1] that arises from post-translational modifications. Even the simplest of enzymatic post-translational modifications, Ser/Thr/Tyr phosphorylation, results in a several-fold increase in the number of forms of a given protein expressed at a given time. Post-translational modifications are dynamic in nature and provide a mechanism whereby cells meet changing growth and signaling needs with a surprisingly small number of genes.

Glycans are added to specific sites on the protein backbone through the actions of glycosyltransferase enzymes under complex control mechanisms (for details see [2]). Unlike the nucleic acids and proteins, glycan biosynthesis occurs without a template. Enzyme and substrate availabilities, among other factors, control the expressed structures of glycoconjugate glycans. As a result, glycans consist of distributions of variations on a core structure, attached to a given aglycon (amino acid residue or lipid core). Viewed in this way, glycosylation vastly increases the complexity of gene products relative to the number of genes in a given eukaryotic genome [1].

Glycoproteins are proteins carrying glycosylation, resulting from enzymatic post-translational modifications. Proteoglycans are a sub-class of glycoproteins in which linear sulfated carbohydrates, known as a glycosaminoglycans (GAGs), are attached to specific Ser residues on the protein backbone through a β-linked Xylose-containing tetrasaccharide. Glycoprotein glycans include the *N*-linked and *O*-linked classes. *N*-Linked glycans modify, through a β-linked GlcNAc, Asn residues in amino acid sequences of NXT or NXS, where X = any residue other than proline. The *N*-linked structure consists of a common chitobiose core $[(GlcNAc)_2(Man)_3]$ and variable branched elaborations forming an antenna structure. Additions of units of lactosamine [Galβ(1-4)GlcNAc] or neo-lactosamine [Galβ(1-3)GlcNAc] capped on the non-reducing end with NeuAc are common to mammalian *N*-linked glycans. The carbohydrate consists of repeating disaccharide units, the biosynthesis of which occurs through the action of a series of glycosylas enzymes. The major classes of *O*-linked glycans are linked through β-*O*-GlcNAc or α-*O*-GalNAc to Ser or Thr residues of the protein backbone. The enzymatic modification of Ser/Thr residues by a single β-*O*-GlcNAc monosaccharide occurs to many nuclear and cytosolic proteins [3-5]. Many of the same Ser and Thr residues that are phosphorylated as part of signal transduction events are also targets for β-*O*-GlcNAc modification. It appears that β-*O*-GlcNAc is a reciprocal switch to phosphorylation and plays important rolse in many intracellular mechanisms. *O*-linked glycans are often branched, sialylated, and typically smaller than *N*-linked glycans. They are bound to Ser or Thr residues, commonly through an α-linked GalNAc residue. *O*-linked glycans are often found in clusters, known as mucin-like domains, along the protein backbone, giving rise to a bottle brush-like structure.

The addition of glycans to the scope of a mass spectrometric analysis scheme entails planning based on clear-eyed understanding of their chemical properties. Native glycans are considerably more fragile than are amino acid chains, and care must be taken to avoid in-source fragmentation during MALDI or ESI MS. Many glycans are capped with sialic acid residues, the glycosidic bonds of which readily dissociate during the MALDI process and during collisional induced dissociation. This phenomenon limits the ability to analyze sialylated glycans using traditional vacuum MALDI with either reflectron TOF or ICR mass analyzers. Any of a number of measures will minimize this problem, including methyl esterification of sialic acids [6, 7], use of anionic MALDI matrix dopants [8, 9], and the use of cooled MALDI sources to diminish the extent to which in-source fragmentation of sialylated glycans occur [10, 11]. Fucose residues also modify many classes of glycans and will fragment readily. Rearrangements of fucose residues have been observed during CID of protonated glycans [12, 13].

Enzymatic addition of sulfate or phosphate groups to specific sites on glycans considerably increases their acidity and fragility during MS ionization and CID. Due to analytical difficulties, the roles of these groups in modulating glycan biological activities have not been fully appreciated. Although FAB mass spectrometry was successfully applied to peptide analysis in the early 1980s, it resulted in abundant fragmentation to glycan sulfate groups, the extent of which increased as the number of sulfations per molecule increased [14].

GAGs are linear oligosaccharides consisting of repeating disaccharide units, as shown in Figure 1. Hyaluronan, an unsulfated GAG not attached to a core protein, consists of repeating units of [GlcAβ(1-3)GlcNAcβ(1-4)], is found in extracellular matrices throughout the animal body, and serves as a tether for glycoproteins and proteoglycans that contain a lectin domain. The size range of hyaluronan is 10^5 to 10^7 Da [2], although smaller fragments are also present in many tissues. Keratan sulfates (KS), unique among GAG classes in that they have Gal instead of HexA residues, are found in many connective tissues. Type I KS, originally described in cornea, is an extension to the type 2 lactosamine [Galβ(1-4)GlcNAc]-containing antennae of *N*-linked glycans. Type II KS, found in skeletal tissue, is an *O*-linked glycan bound to Ser or Thr residues through a αGalNAc residue. KS chains are usually sulfated on the 6-position of GlcNAc and may be sulfated on the 6-position of Gal residues. KS chains often have specialized capping sequence on the non-reducing chain ends, the complexities of which vary among different tissues [15-18]. For example, while neuraminic acids in either the α(2-3) or α(2-6) linkage cap KS in skeletal tissue, considerably more variable capping structures have been observed for corneal KS. In addition, α(1-3) fucose substituted onto GlcNAc residues has been observed for articular cartilage KS.

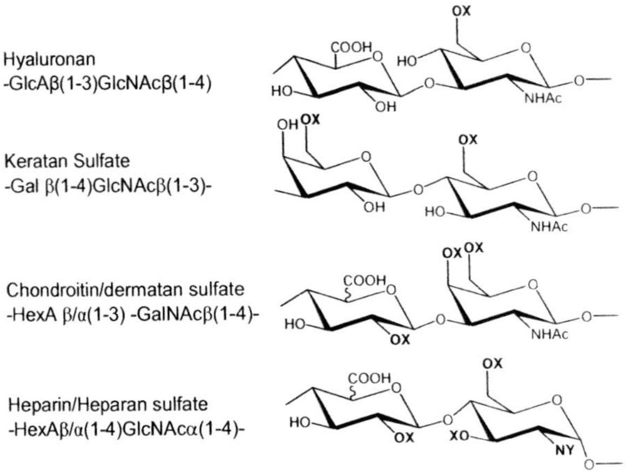

Figure 1. Disaccharide Repeating Structures for the Glycosaminoglycans. The possible positions of sulfation are indicated for each GAG class. X = H or SO_3H, Y = H or Ac or SO_3H.

Chondroitin sulfate (CS) consists of repeating units of [GlcAβ(1-3)GalNAcβ(1-4)] enzymatically polymerized on a protein-bound linker oligosaccharide of the sequence GlcAβ(1,3)Galβ(1,3)Galβ(1,4)-Xylβ(1-*O*)-Ser. Once polymerized, sulfotransferase and uronic acid epimerases modify the nascent chains to form mature CS with domains of high content of GlcA alternating with those containing high content of IdoA residues. Dermatan sulfate (DS), a form of CS, contains a high content of IdoA residues and a given chain will have CS-like domains alternating with DS-like domains. CS sequences are commonly sulfated on the 4- and/or 6-positions of GalNAc residues and less commonly at the 2-position of GlcA residues. DS sequences are commonly sulfated at the 4-position of GalNAc residues and less commonly at the 2-position of IdoA residues [19]. DS sequences are of biochemical interest because the high IdoA content confers conformational flexibility that facilitates interactions with protein binding partners (20).

The heparan sulfates (HS) are the most highly sulfated, complex, and information-rich of the GAGs [for a reviews see [21, 22]]. Biosynthetic enzymes polymerize repeats of [GlcAβ(1-4)GlcNAcα(1-4)] onto a linker of the same structure as CS/DS GAGs, and the same Ser residue may be modified with CS or HS chains under different conditions [23]. After biosynthesis, *N*-deacetylase/*N*-sulfotransferase enzymes act on the nascent chains to create alternating domains with high content of *N*-sulfated GlcN residues and those with high content of GlcNAc residues. Epimerases then convert many of the GlcA residues to IdoA and specific sulfotransferases modify the 3- and/or 6-positions of GlcN-sulfate residues and/or the 2-position of IdoA residues. These enzymatic modifications result in alternating *N*-acetylated domains with high GlcNAc and low sulfation and *N*-sulfated domains with high sulfation and epimerization. The enzymatic reactions do not go to completion, therefore, no two HS chains have exactly the same pattern of sulfation and epimerization. Heparin, a highly sulfated form of HS found in mast cell granules, contains a comparatively low content of *N*-acetylated domains. HS chains bound to syndecan and glypican core proteins coat the surfaces of all adherent animal cells, and bound to perlecan, agrin and other molecules play roles in extracellular matrices [for reviews see [22, 24, 25]]. The considerable ongoing biomedical interest in HS stems from the many classes of growth factors and growth factor receptors that bind to these molecules [26]. The HS sequences that bind to proteins of interest have been determined in only a few cases due to analytical difficulties. HS chains appear to serve as cell surface co-receptors that catalyze interactions of growth factors and growth factor receptors by virtue of their ability to bind both partners [27]. HS bound to extracellular matrix molecules appears to act by binding growth factors and setting up gradients for these molecules that are necessary for cell migration [28, 29].

Polysulfation confers chemical properties on the GAGs that dictate modification of the mass spectrometric techniques that have become standard for analysis of peptides and *N*- and *O*-linked oligosaccharides. Sulfate group fragility drives the need for gentle ionization conditions to prevent in-source fragmentation of these molecules. The value of tandem mass spectra generated from polysulfated oligosaccharides depends on the charge state of the precursor ion to a greater extent than observed for less acidic biological macromolecules (peptides and other glycan classes). The sections below summarize mass spectrometric approaches for analysis of sulfated GAGs. Although space limitations do not permit an exhaustive review of the literature, emphasis is given to the techniques that have proven the most practical for GAG analysis.

4. Techniques for GAG Analysis

a. Molecular Weight Measurement of Intact GAG Chains

Hyaluronan is a non-sulfated GAG that plays important roles in extracellular matrices through tethering glycoproteins and proteoglycans to cell surfaces. Oligosaccharides produced from hyaluronan have been used to characterize interactions with binding proteins. In some cases, low molecular weight fractions of hyaluronan have biological activities not associated with the parent molecule (reviewed in [30]). These observations have catalyzed efforts to generate methods for production of hyaluronan olgosaccharides in high purity. One such method combines SEC and high performance anion exchange chromatography [30]. ESI has been used effectively in the characterization of hyaluronan oligomers [30-32]. Negative ESI is a natural choice for hyaluronan fragments due the high uronic acid content.

Sulfated GAGs are polydisperse with respect to chain length and sulfate content, resulting in a distribution of glycoforms for a chain bound to a given Ser residue. Although it is possible to produce abundant ions from intact GAG chains using negative ESI, the polydispersity and high mass results in a complex pattern of overlapping charge states. This effect may be seen clearly with a quadrupole mass analyzer. Fourier transform MS has sufficient resolving power to separate isotopes and identify charge states for ions produced from molecules as large as GAGs (up to ~50 kDa) but is limited by space charge effects. Thus, an intact crude GAG sample will produce so many different *m/z* values that none is above the noise level. Determination of intact GAG chains using FTMS will require some preliminary chromatographic separation or ion filtering to limit the number of *m/z* values produced in a single spectrum.

The use of capillary and slab electrophoresis for the analysis of GAGs has recently been reviewed [33, 34]. Gradient polyacrylamide gel electrophoresis has been used to characterize GAGs in urine of mucopolysaccharidosis patients [35]. The value of slab gel electrophoresis is that it provides an estimation of the molecular weight distribution for these very complex samples. GAGs may be blotted onto cationic nitrocellulose membranes, a technique that potentially allows subsequent manipulation of the samples [36]. GAGs are similar to nucleic acids in that they are linear and anionic. Like nucleic acids, GAG chains may be separated using polyacrylamide gel electrophoresis with laser induced fluorescence detection. Unlike nucleic acids, sulfated GAGs are extremely polydisperse, and clear bands are not observed.

SEC has been widely used to determine the average size distributions in GAG preparations (for examples see [37-43]). GAG behavior during SEC separation has been shown to be distinct from that of proteins [44]. A method for determination of the average molecular weight of heparin preparations using SEC with universal calibration has been described [45].

b. GAG Degrading Enzymes

GAG degrading enzymes and their activities have been reviewed [46]. To give a brief background, GAGs are commonly depolymerized through the use of commercially available enzymes of two varieties. GAG lyase enzymes act through an eliminative mechanism to cleave a HexNAc-HexA bond, leaving a (4,5)-unsaturated (termed Δ-unsaturated) HexA residue at the new non-reducing terminus. GAG endohydrolase enzymes act by a hydrolytic mechanism to produce saturated residues at both the new reducing and non-reducing ends. For hyaluronan, testicular hyaluronidase is an effective endohydrolase enzyme for depolymerization.that cleaves the GlcNAc-GlcA bond (for a brief review see [30]). Testicular hyaluronidase also cleaves CS, albeit slowly. This enzyme is reported to have transglycosylase activity [47-50] and for this reason is not used for structural analysis of CS. For keratan sulfate, keratanase (from *Pseudomonas*), and keratanase II (from *Bacillus sp. Ks36*) enzymes are available. Keratanase is an endo-β-1,4-galactosidase that requires an unsulfated Gal residue flanked by 6-*O*-sulfated GlcNAc residues. Keratanase II is an endo-β-1,3-glucosaminidase that requires sulfation at the 6-*O* position of GlcN, but acts independently of Gal sulfation. Thus, it cleaves at a majority of 6-*O*-sulfated GlcNAc residues. For an overview of the use of keratanases for structural profiling of KS, see [18]. Each of the five commercially available chondroitin lyase enzymes cleave the GalNAc-HexA bond by an eliminative mechanism. Chondroitinase ABC, from *Proteus vulgaris*, is non-specific and cleaves all forms of CS. Chondroitinase ACI, purified from *Flavobacterium heparinum*, cleaves GalNAc-GlcA bonds in which GalNAc is 4- or 6-*O*-sulfated but is inactive against GalNAc-IdoA bonds. Chondroitinase ACI is active against the GlcA containing regions of CS/DS co-polymers. Chondroitinase ACII is purified from the culture broth of *Arthrobacter aurescens* and has similar activity but does not act on CS/DS co-polymers. Chondroitinase ACII is active against hyaluronan. Chondroitinase B cleaves GalNAc-IdoA bonds. Chondroitinase C is specific for GalNAc-GlcA bonds in which the GalNAc residue is 4-*O*-sulfated.

Enzymatic depolymerization of HS and heparin is discussed in detail in [26]. Three commercially available heparin lyases are available, each of which cleaves the GlcN-HexA bond in HS/heparin. Heparin lyase I, from *Flavobacterium heparinum*, cleaves highly sulfated regions, known as *N*-sulfated regions, of HS/heparin. Heparin lyase III, from *Flavobacterium heparinum*, cleaves regions with high content of GlcNAc residues. Heparin lyase II, from *Flavobacterium heparinum*, has some activity for *N*-acetylated regions and some for *N*-sulfated regions. HS/heparin may also be chemically cleaved using nitrous acid treatment. Nitrous acid at pH <2.5 cleaves *N*-sulfated GlcN residues, forming anhydromannose and leaving the uronic acid residue intact [51]. In this regard, nitrous acid is complementary to lyase digestion. Details on the use and mechanism of nitrous acid cleavage are given in [26].

d. Determination of GAG Depolymerization Products

The average chain length of GAG chains may be determined by quantifying the non-reducing or reducing terminal saccharides relative to those in the interior of the sequence. Lyase depolymerization results in the formation of a disaccharide containing a saturated HexA residue, corresponding to the non-reducing terminus of the intact chain. An ion exchange HPLC method for quantification of the non-reducing terminal saccharides relative to interior disaccharides resulting from lyase digestion has been used to estimate the size of CS chains [52, 53]. More recently, fluorophore-assisted carbohydrate electrophoresis has been used to characterize GAG depolymerization products [30, 54-56]. The method has the advantage of high sensitivity, due to the fluorescence of the 2-aminoacridone label used. This technique is similar in capability to capillary electrophoresis with laser induced fluorescence detection used for GAG disaccharide analysis [57-60]. More details on GAG disaccharide analysis are given in section 0.

e. GAG Sequencing

Analytical techniques for sequencing of HS/heparin oligosaccharides have been reviewed [26, 61, 62]. Generally, techniques involve isolation of GAG chains from a biological source followed by partial depolymerization and purification of an oligosaccharide of interest using affinity chromatography. Labeling of the oligosaccharides with a radioisotope, chromophore or fluorophore allows sensitive detection of the GAG oligosaccharides. Alternatively, cultured cells can be metabolically labeled with $^{35}SO_3$. The purified, labeled oligosaccharides are then subjected to further enzymatic and/or chemical cleavage and detection of the products using HPLC or electrophoresis [61, 63, 64]. These approaches carry the advantage that they have proven successful at sequencing selected GAG oligosaccharides from cellular sources.

5. Mass Spectrometric Ionization of GAG Oligosaccharides

The energetic nature of the desolvation process in early ESI sources resulted in similar problems to FAB MS, with intact ions from polysulfated glycans observed only in low abundances. Once optimized sources became available, however, the usefulness of ESI for the analysis of sulfated glycans became clear and the development of tandem mass spectrometric methods for determination of the structures of sulfated glycans became possible [65-71]. Traditional vacuum MALDI results in the deposition of a considerable amount of internal energy into analyte ions, and this causes very weak molecular ion signals for polysulfated glycans. The addition of basic peptides to pair with polysulfated glycans overcomes this problem and results in the detection of a peptide-oligosaccharide complex [72, 73].

The pKa of a typical sulfate group is ~3, rendering the sulfated GAGs the most acidic biomolecules. Although this property suggests the use of negative mode ionization, the engineering of mass spectrometers and orientation of mass spectrometrists tends toward the positive mode. This inclination goes a long way towards explaining the history of mass spectrometric analysis of sulfated GAGs in which the use of positive ionization resulted in very limited success toward the production of intact molecular ions. Fast atom bombardment (FAB), also known as liquid secondary ionization, was applied to the analysis of HS [74-79] and CS [75, 80] chains during the same timeframe as to peptides, in the early 1980s. In general, FAB ionization resulted in fragmentation to the sulfate groups and the observation of intact molecular ions in low abundances. At the same time, permethylated glycans [81] derived from a variety of glycoconjugates were observed to produce significantly stronger signals than their native counterparts [82-84].

a. MALDI of GAG Oligosaccharides

In the early days of MALDI, researchers observed that acidic biomolecules produce very weak intact molecular ions in either the positive or negative ionization modes [73]. After several years of work, it became clear that all biomolecules tend to undergo fragmentation in the MALDI source under vacuum conditions [85, 86], and that native oligosaccharides undergo this process to a significantly greater extent than do peptides [87]. Sialylated oligosaccharides pose a particular problem using vacuum MALDI, as shown by the fact that intact molecular ions cannot be transmitted through the ion reflector, indicating that metastable decay occurs in the first field free region [7]. Sulfate groups confer an even greater fragility when present on an oligosaccharide structure [72]. Figure 2 illustrates the tendency for protonated sulfate groups to dissociate as the internal energy increases during ionization or a dissociation experiment. During CID, deprotonated sulfate groups or those paired with a metal cation tend not to fragment to produce losses of SO_3 from the precursor ion and require significantly higher energies to undergo fragmentation than do protonated sulfate groups [14].

Hyaluronan lacks sulfation, and MALD mass spectrometric approaches are similar to those used for other acidic polysaccharide classes. MALDI approaches for carbohydrates have been reviewed [88, 89]. Use of negative MALDI-TOF MS in linear [90] or reflectron mode [91, 92] from 2,5-dihydroxybenzoic acid (DHB) matrix to profile hyaluronidase digestion products of hyaluronan resulted in detection of $[M-H]^-$ ions with no evidence of fragmentation of the ions. In the negative reflectron mode, DP4, 6 and 8 were detected, while in the positive mode only the DP4 was detected. The same MALDI conditions resulted in fragmentation to the sulfate groups of CS oligosaccharides [91]. Linear negative MALDI-TOF MS from DHB matrix was used to profile complex hyaluronan digest mixtures after separation by SEC [93]. Other researchers prefer 2,4,6-trihydroxyacetophenone/ammonium citrate matrix for negative reflectron MALDI of HA oligosaccharides [30], and the choice of matrix may depend on the instrument used. Reductive amination using anthanilic acid was found to enhance the negative MALDI signal strength from DHB matrix of mixtures of hyaloronan oligosaccharides (94). The reflectron mode was found to be effective for profiling DP4-10 and the linear mode most appropriate for DP12-36. In summary, the use of negative MALDI for profiling hyaluronan oligosaccharides is a well-established method.

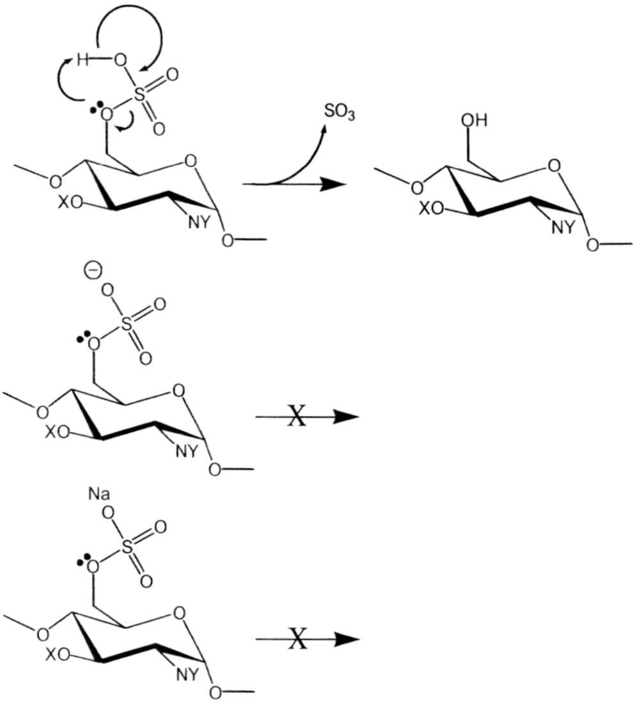

Figure 2. Production of abundant ions from losses of SO_3 in sulfated oligosaccharides during CID. X = SO_3H or H, Y = Ac or SO_3H or H.

Direct MALDI-TOF MS analysis of CS oligosaccharides using DHB matrix has shown results similar to those using FAB ionization [91] in that fragmentation to the sulfate groups was evident in the mass spectra. Chondroitin lyase degradation products analyzed as both positive and negative ions from DHB matrix showed fragmentation to the sulfate groups through losses of 102 u ($NaSO_3$) [91]. The use of positive linear mode MALDI-TOF MS from DHB matrix has been reported for CS oligosaccharides [95]. Multiply sodiated ions were detected, and it is likely that sulfate groups were lost during the ionization process. The basic peptide $(RG)_{15}$ has been used for positive MALDI-TOF MS analysis of CS oligosaccharides from caffeic acid matrix [96]. The use of basic peptides for the MALDI-TOF MS analysis of polysulfated GAG oligosaccharides is strongly recommended (details on this method are given below).

The addition of basic peptides or proteins to the matrix mixture containing polysulfated oligosaccharides results in the observation of a complex in positive mode MALDI MS [72, 73]. These complexes evidently arise from pairing of negatively charged sulfate groups with positively charged arginine or lysine residues, and the *m/z* value of the protein-oligosaccharide complex provides a means of molecular weight determination given the known protein mass. Measuring the masses of HS oligosaccharides using this approach before and after digestion with enzymes of known specificities provides an effective means of sequencing these molecules [97-100]. The observed *m/z* values for protein-carbohydrate complexes provides a means of determining the ability of a given HS oligosaccharide to bind a basic protein (growth factor) molecule using positive mode MALDI-TOF MS [101, 102]. Alternatively, as shown in Figure 2, pairing a sodium or other alkali cation with a sulfate group also stabilizes it during the ionization or CID process.

The use of MALDI-TOF MS to characterize GAGs and their interactions with proteins has recently been reviewed [103]. The most effective uses of MALDI-TOF MS for analysis of sulfated GAGs involve pairing the oligosaccharide to a basic peptide or protein, thereby minimizing the extent of in-source fragmentation. Measurement of HS oligosaccharide mass typically involves the use of the synthetic peptide $(RG)_{19}R$, isolated as the free base [100]. Caffeic acid matrix has proven effective for the observation of GAG-peptide complexes in the positive mode. Measurement of oligosaccharide mass before and after enzymatic or chemical degradation is a useful means of sequence determination [97-100, 104]. This approach has been used to study the binding of HS sequences to fibroblastic growth factors [104, 105]. The detection of intact proteins bound to a GAG oligosaccharide has been used to study growth factor oligomerization [102]. Mass spectrometric analysis of protein-GAG complexes has been reviewed in detail elsewhere [14].

b. ESI of GAG Oligosaccharides

Comparisons of the use of negative ESI and negative MALDI for analysis of hyaluronan oligosaccharides points out the importance of mass spectrometric operating parameters for success of the experiment [106, 107]. The use of ESI desolvation conditions that are appropriate for peptides will result in fragmentation to the HA oligosaccharides, with the result that ions corresponding to the loss of a monosaccharide residue from the oligosaccharides are detected. This in-source fragmentation may be eliminated by reducing the magnitude to the electrospray desolvation voltages. It is the author's experience that sources producing slow heating of the electrospray droplets (heated capillary sources or Z-spray) result in the most gentle desolvation. This is particularly important for analysis of polysulfated oligosaccharides. An LC/MS of system for analysis of hyaluronan oligosaccharides has been described that employs a C2 column for separation [107].

Observation of intact ions from sulfated GAG oligosaccharides using ESI requires special care despite the gentle nature of this ionization technique relative to vacuum MALDI. Desolvation conditions optimized for the analysis of peptides in the positive mode will surely cause in-source fragmentation of sulfated oligosaccharides. Greater success results from switching to the negative mode and using the lowest (in absolute terms) desolvation energies possible. In addition, the use of a solution containing ammonium sulfate [108], ammonium acetate [109], or ammonium hydroxide [110] is recommended. Negative ESI results in the observation of intact molecular ions, enabling tandem mass spectrometric experiments using this ionization mode. The production of positive ions by pairing polysulfated oligosaccharides with cationic counter ions has been demonstrated using ESI [111] and applied to on-line LC/MS using reversed phase ion pairing chromatography [112, 113], as discussed in detail in section 0. While cationic ion paring is useful for conducting LC-MS analyses in positive ion mode, it is not useful in MS/MS analysis, due to the absence of oligosaccharide backbone cleavage products.

6. MASS SPECTROMETRIC GAG DISACCHARIDE PROFILING

Analysis of an unknown GAG sample entails determining the composition of the products of complete enzymatic degradation, often achieved using chondroitin or heparin lyase enzymes. Non-specific chondroitin lyase digestion of a CS/DS proteoglycan or released GAG sample results in the formation of the eight Δ-unsaturated structures shown in Table 1. Complete lyase digestion of a HS/heparin sample results in the formation of 12 Δ-unsaturated disaccharides, see Table 2. Note that in producing a 4,5-unsaturated uronic acid residue, the action of the lyase enzyme destroys the epimeric center in position 5. Several techniques will separate and quantify Δ-unsaturated lyase mixtures, including ion exchange, normal phase and reversed phase ion pairing chromatography [114]. The most sensitive methods of disaccharide analysis entail detection of fluorescent disaccharide derivatives. Capillary electrophoresis with laser-induced fluorescence detection (60, 115) or fluorescence assisted carbohydrate electrophoresis [54-56] of reductively aminated disaccharides with the 2-aminoacridone label have both proven effective for quantitative analysis. Separation of disaccharides using reversed phase ion pairing chromatography followed by post-column derivatization with 2-cyanoacetamide and fluorescence detection [116, 117] provides sufficient sensitivity for the analysis of CS/DS and HS disaccharides released from *Drosophila* and *C. elegans* preparations [118, 119] and has been used in a number of other biochemical studies [120-122].

Mass spectrometric determination of Δ-unsaturated disaccharides entails the use of a combination of MS and MS^n scans on an ion trap instrument. This approach hinges on the determination of the ionization response of each disaccharide relative to an internal standard to enable calculation of a correction factor for the raw ion abundances. Quantification of disaccharides with unique molecular masses entails determination of the corrected ion abundances relative to that of the internal standard. Tandem MS is necessary for isomeric disaccharides, and product ions uniquely abundant to a given structure must be identified using pure standards. The abundances of these ions in isomeric mixtures are used to quantify the composition of a mixture of isomers using a system of equations [123, 124]. This approach has been adapted for the analysis of CS [108, 125] and HS [126] disaccharides. Consider for example the Δ-unsaturated disaccharides derived from CS/DS, shown in Table 1. Distinct product ions that distinguish each of the three isomeric singly sulfated disaccharides ΔDi-UA2S, ΔDi-4S and ΔDi-6S [127] are listed in the table. The abundances of the three diagnostic product ions (*m/z* 237, 282, and 300 as shown in Table 1) for pure standards are used to mathematically determine the composition of the three disaccharides in a mixture based on the abundances of the diagnostic ions using a system of equations [108]. Although the published work has been limited to the singly sulfated CS/DS Δ-unsaturated disaccharides, the same principle will likely determine the compositions of mixtures containing the isomeric di-sulfated disaccharides shown in Table 1.

Lyase digestion of HS/heparin results in 12 possible Δ-unsaturated disaccharides, as shown in Table 2. Those disaccharides with the –A suffix are *N*-acetylated, –S are *N*-sulfated, and –H are unmodified GlcN residues [26]. The –A and –S disaccharides compose the bulk of lyase digestion products, with –H structures in very low abundances [128]. Mass spectrometric quantification of the isomeric III-A, II-A pair and the III-S, II-S pair [126] involves an approach similar to that used for the CS oligosaccharides, described above. Tandem mass spectrometry of pure II-A shows an abundant $^{0,2}A_2$ ion while that of III-A an abundant B_1 ion (see Table 2), useful for determining mixture compositions. Although the II-S disaccharide ion produces an abundant Y_1 as a diagnostic, the III-S disaccharide ion does not produce a useful ion in the MS^2 stage. Subsequent fragmentation of the $^{0,2}A_2$ ion (247.5→357.0) results in the formation of the diagnostic $^{2,4}A_2$ ion. Thus, tandem mass spectrometry using an ion trap based on ion abundances in the MS, MS^2 or MS^3 stages provides a means of quantification of HS/heparin disaccharides relative to a single internal standard. Presumably, similar methods will distinguish the –H disaccharides shown in Table 2.

Table 1. Structures of Δ-unsaturated CS/DS disaccharides, and diagnostic mass spectrometric ions useful for quantitation [108]. ND = not determined

Disaccharide	Structure	Mass	MS mode	Diagnostic ion	m/z
ΔDi-OS	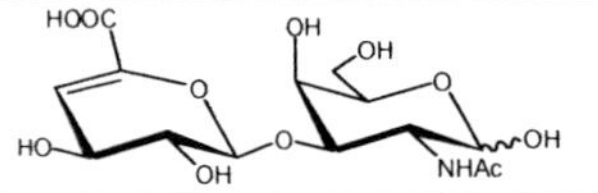	379.11	MS	$[M-H]^-$	378.1
ΔDi-4S	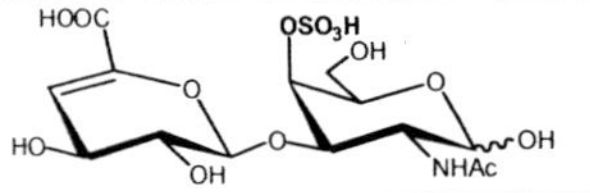	459.07	MS^2	Y_1	300.0
ΔDi-6S	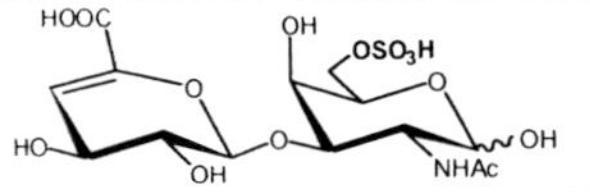	459.07	MS^2	Z_1	282.0
ΔDi-UA2S	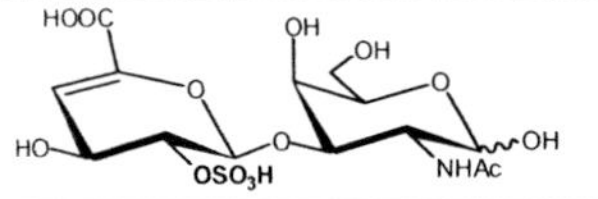	459.07	MS^2	B_1	237.0
ΔDi-S_B	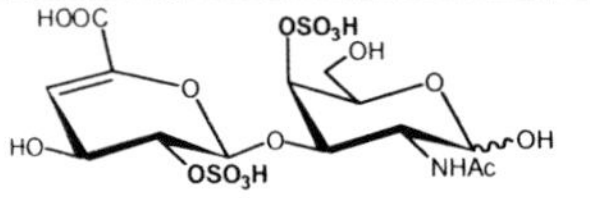	539.03	ND		
ΔDi-S_D	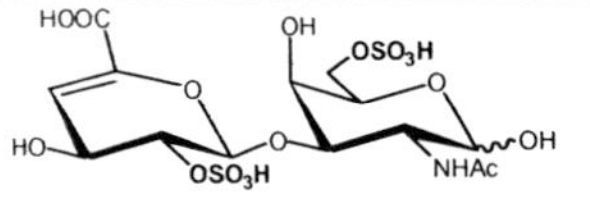	539.03	ND		
ΔDi-S_E	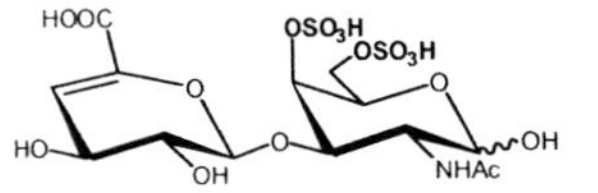	539.03	ND		
ΔDi-TriS	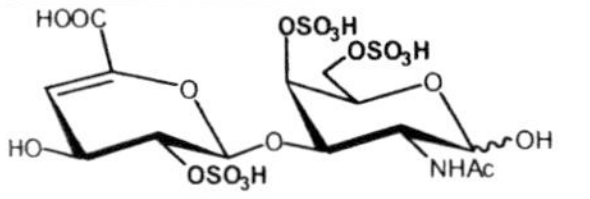	618.98	ND		

Table 2. Structures of Δ-unsaturated HS/heparin disaccharides, and diagnostic mass spectrometric ions useful for quantitation [126]. ND = not determined

Disaccharide	Structure	Mass	MS mode	Diagnostic ion	m/z
HS IV-A	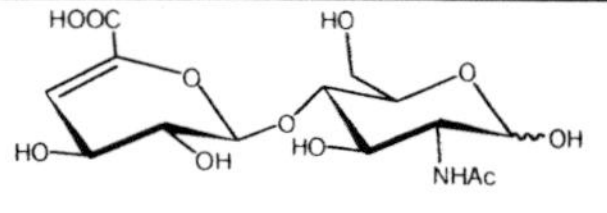	379.11	MS	$[M-H]^-$	378.1
HS III-A	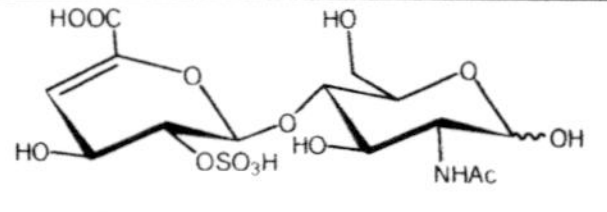	459.07	MS^2	B_1	237.0
HS II-A	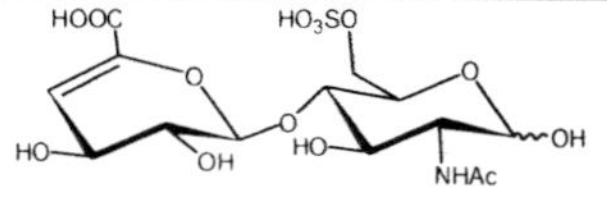	459.07	MS^2	$^{0,2}A_2$	357.1
HS I-A	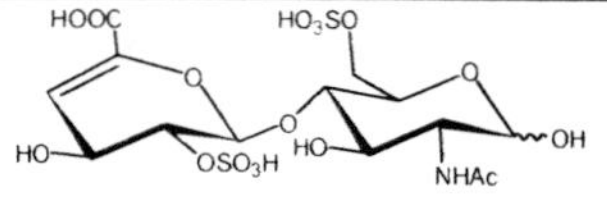	539.03	MS	$[M-2H]^{2-}$	268.5
HS IV-S	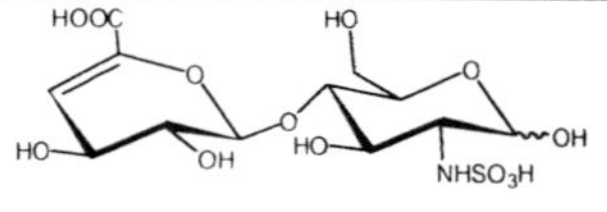	417.06	MS	$[M-H]^-$	416.0
HS III-S	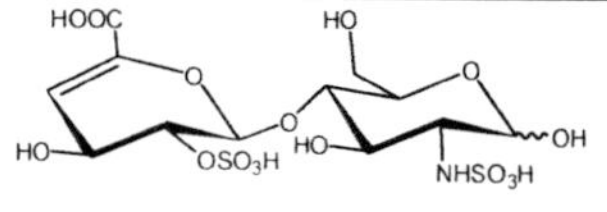	497.01	MS^3	$^{2,4}A_2$	247.5^{2-} → 357.0
HS II-S	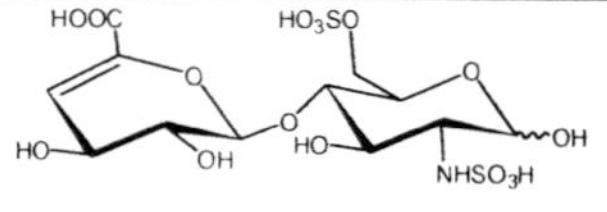	497.01	MS^2	Y_1	338.0
HS I-S	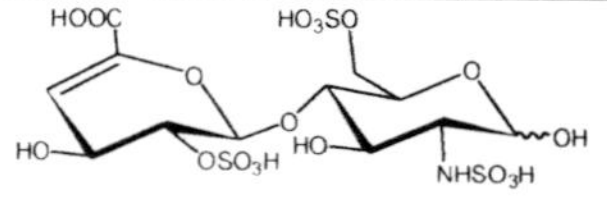	576.97	MS	$[M-H]^-$	576.0
HS IV-H	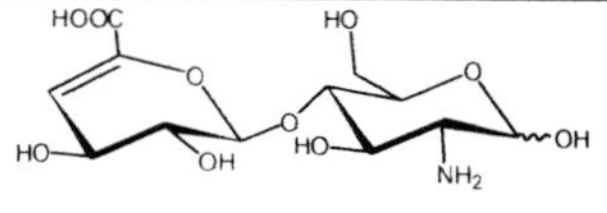	337.10	ND		
HS III-H	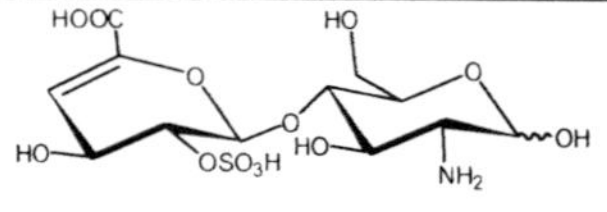	417.06	ND		
HS II-H	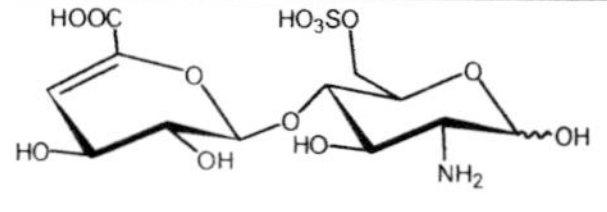	417.06	ND		
HS I-H	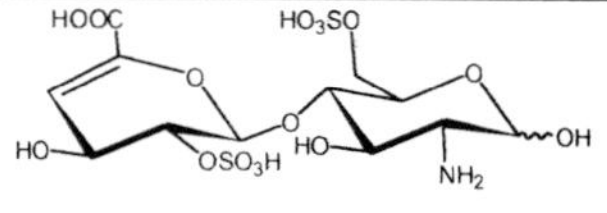	497.01	ND		

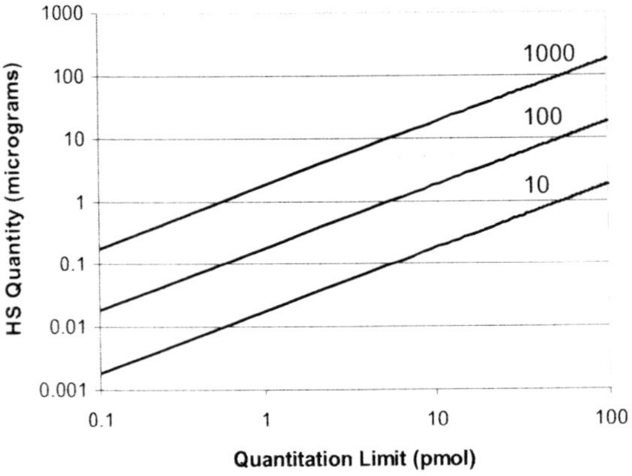

Figure 3. Total quantity of HS required for disaccharide analysis as a function of analytical detection limit and range of disaccharide concentrations. The three curves show 1000:1, 100:1, and 10:1 ranges in the concentrations of the most:least abundant disaccharides

The amount of HS required for disaccharide analysis depends on the limit of quantification of the analytical detection technique and on the range of concentration between the most abundant disaccharide and the least. As shown in Figure 3, a quantity of 2 μg of HS is required with an analytical detection limit of 1 pmol of disaccharide if the range of the constituent disaccharide concentrations varies over a factor of 1000. CE with laser-induced detection generates effective detection limits in this range for reductively aminated disaccharides [60, 115]. Note that the sample quantity limitations arise due to sample handling issues and not to the absolute sensitivity of the detector. For analysis of GAGs from small organisms such as *Drosophila*, sub-microgram quantities may be available and only the HPLC method with post-column 2-cyanoacetamide derivatization and fluorescence detection has demonstrated the sensitivity required for these samples [129]. Although mass spectrometric quantification requires no derivatization or workup of the enzymatically produced disaccharide mixture (108), the detection limits remain untested and the method has not yet been used for analysis of small quantities of GAG samples. Given the known performance of modern electrospray mass spectrometers, however, detection limits of 1 pmol per disaccharide or better seem reasonable. If so, then mass spectrometric quantification will compete with CE/LIF in terms of sensitivity.

7. Tandem MS of Sulfated GAGs

Although FAB ionization produced the first tandem mass spectra of sulfated GAGs [127, 130, 131], the singly charged ions fragmented by losing SO_3 from the precursor ions, diminishing the diagnostic value of the product ion pattern. ESI, however, results in multiple charging and the formation of glycosidic bond cleavages. The product ion patterns resulting from CID of multiply charged negative GAG oligosaccharide ions differ depending on the GAG oligosaccharide class, allowing for their analysis.

Chondroitin/dermatan sulfate. Commercially available chondroitin lyase enzymes act to cleave CS/DS chains to the reducing side of HexNAc residues by an eliminative mechanism to generate cleavage products with Δ-unsaturated uronic acid at the non-reducing terminus. The unsaturated bond absorbs at 232 nm, allowing precise control of the extent of enzymatic digestion. Tandem mass spectrometric fragmentation of Δ-unsaturated CS disaccharides results in an abundant $^{0,2}X_1$ ion that arises from rearrangement of the unsaturated uronic acid ring. CS/DS oligosaccharides also produce an analogous ion albeit at lower relative abundance.

The product ion patterns of CS/DS oligosaccharide ions change dramatically with charge state, as shown in Figure 4 [132]. With only one charge, two sulfate groups remain protonated for the $[M-H]^-$ ion, and fragmentation to the sulfate groups dominates the product ion profile. Glycosidic bond cleavage ions become significantly more abundant for the $[M-2H]^{2-}$ ion, and are most abundant to the reducing side of the GalNAc residues, similar to those observed adjacent to HexNAc residues in other classes of oligosaccharides [133]. This pattern changes dramatically during fragmentation of the $[M-3H]^{3-}$ charge state in that glycosidic cleavage is produced to the non-reducing side of the GalNAc residue. Evidently, the most labile glycosidic bond is no longer to the reducing side of the GalNAc residue, as is typical for glycans. Interestingly, the abundances of the glycosidic bond cleavages depend on the positions of GalNAc sulfation and uronic acid epimerization [134]. The usefulness of tandem MS for structural analysis of CS oligosaccharides has now been shown in a number of applications [135-137]. CS/DS oligosaccharides tend to form negative electrospray ions in which the most abundant corresponds to one charge per sulfate group, resulting in the formation of abundant ions from glycosidic bond cleavages with low abundances for ions from fragmentation to the sulfate groups [132, 138].

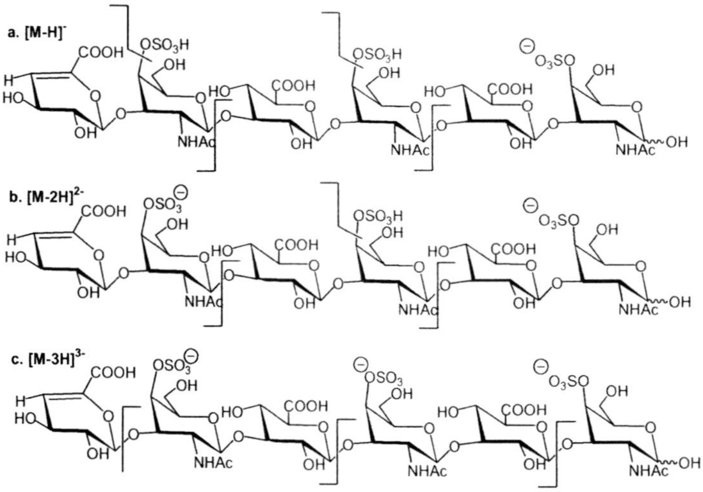

Figure 4. The effect of charge state on product ion pattern for CS/DS oligosaccharides. (a) $[M-H]^-$, (b) $[M-2H]^{2-}$, (c) $[M-3H]^{3-}$. The structures shown correspond to CSA-type (GlcA, GalNAc4S) and Similar trends are observed for oligosaccharides of different lengths and those derived from CSB/DS (IdoA, GalNAc4S) and CSC (GlcA, GalNAc6S). The most abundant bond cleavage ions are shown

Figure 5 illustrates the general trends for the dependence of negative ESI product ion pattern on deprotonated precursor ion charge in the tandem mass spectra of CS/DS oligosaccharides, combining data from the published literature [14, 108, 125, 132, 134, 136, 139, 140]. For the $[M-H]^-$ ion generated from a tetra-sulfated CS octamer, three of the four sulfate groups remain protonated, and the ion carries the equivalent of 0.125 charge per monosaccharide residue. Under these conditions, the most abundant product ion results from loss of SO_3 from the precursor. For the same octamers, $[M-4H]^{4-}$ ions have one charge per sulfate group, corresponding to 0.5 charge per monosaccharide residue and produce abundant glycosidic bond fragmentation with very low abundances for losses of SO_3. Note that losses of SO_3 are more abundant for GalNAc-6-sulfated CS than for GalNAc-4-sulfated CS/DS [134]. The 5- charge state for a CS/DS tetrasulfated octamer corresponds to 0.625 charge per monosaccharide residue and results in a useful product ion pattern with slightly elevated losses of the equivalent of $[H_2SO_4]^-$. As a general trend, the abundances of such losses increasee with increasing absolute value of negative charge state.

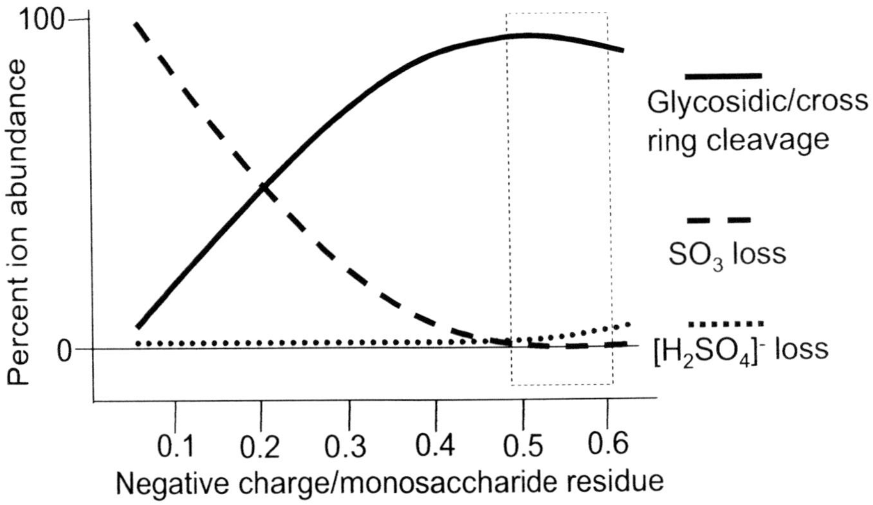

Figure 5. Trends in fragmentation types observed for CS oligosaccharides as a function of charge state. The plots are constructed from published CS/DS tandem mass spectrometric data and represent general trends rather than exact product ion abundances. The rectangle highlights the region of precursor ion negative charge/residue observed to produce the most useful product ion patterns

Keratan sulfates. For the analysis of KS chains there exist two commercially available glycosidase enzymes, keratanase and keratanase II. Keratanase is an endo-β-galactosidase, cleaving to the reducing side of unsulfated Gal residues and keratanase II is an endo-β-*N*-acetylglucosaminidase, cleaving to the reducing side of 6-*O*-sulfated GlcNAc residues, acting independently of sulfation to Gal residues. Both enzymes act by a hydrolytic mechanism to produce fully saturated oligosaccharides. Use of similar negative ion electrospray mass spectrometric conditions for KS oligosaccharides as used for CS/DS results in the production of ions in which all sulfate groups are charged. While, relative to CS/DS, KS oligosaccharides contain a similar number of sulfate groups per disaccharide repeat, they produce markedly different product ion patterns. Most oligosaccharides containing a reducing terminal 4-linked HexNAc residue produce an abundant $^{0,2}A_n$ cross-ring cleavage ion [141, 142], and KS oligosaccharides follow this rule. The cross-ring cleavage mechanism entails anomeric ring opening followed by a retro-aldol rearrangement that requires a free 3-hydroxyl group [141, 143], therefore, the 3-linked GalNAc residue on the reducing terminus of lyase-generated CS/DS oligosaccharides does not produce this $^{0,2}A_n$ ion [144]. In addition, KS oligosaccharides fragment to produce an abundant ion from loss of water from the precursor ion [145, 146]. Isolation and MS^3 fragmentation of the $[M-H_2O]$ ion results in abundant and useful glycosidic bond cleavage ions [147]. Thus, the use of trapped ion mass spectrometers will achieve best results for analysis of KS oligosaccharides.

Heparan sulfates. Commercially available heparin lyases cleave HS chains by an eliminative mechanism to the reducing side of GlcN residues, creating a Δ-unsaturated HexA residue at the new non-reducing end. The absorbance of the unsaturated bond provides a means of controlling the extent of reaction precisely. Tandem mass spectrometric analysis of HS Δ-unsaturated disaccharides demonstrates that abundant $^{0,2}X_1$ ions are formed in addition to glycosidic bond and $^{0,2}A_2$ ions from cleavage of the 4-linked reducing terminal HexN residue [126]. The $^{0,2}X_1$ ions result from a retro-Diels-Alder rearrangement and the $^{0,2}A_2$ from anomeric ring opening followed by retro-aldol rearrangement [144].

Studies on synthetic heparin oligosaccharides have shown that the product ion pattern depends strongly on the precursor ion charge state. In a manner similar to that observed for CS/DS oligosaccharides, HS oligosaccharide ions with low negative charge states (in absolute value terms) contain several protonated sulfate groups and the most abundant product ions result from losses of SO_3 from the precursor ion [148]. Although the relative abundances of glycosidic bond cleavage product ions increases with higher negative charge states (absolute value terms), the abundances of other sulfate group fragmentations also increase. For oligosaccharides with triply sulfated GlcN residues, the abundances of ions produced from losses of the equivalent of $[H_2SO_4]^-$ increase as the precursor ion charge increases [149]. Fragmentations to the sulfate groups thus compete with glycosidic bond cleavages during the CID process for deprotonated HS oligosaccharides, entailing special care in interpreting the mass spectral profiles. The only way to insure that an observed product ion has not undergone secondary fragmentation to a sulfate group is through the detection of a complementary ion. The sum of the neutral mass equivalents of an ion and its complement total the mass of the neutral molecule. Alternatively, the pairing of alkali or alkaline earth metals with heparin oligosaccharides results in sulfate group stabilization, preventing both losses of SO_3 and the equivalent of $[H_2SO_4]^-$ to a large extent [148].Figure **6** illustrates the general trend for the effects of charge state on the observed product ion profiles. Precursor ions with fewer than 0.5 charge per monosaccharide residue have several sulfate groups that remain protonated, and losses of SO_3 dominate the product ion profiles. The formation of ions with approximately one charge per monosaccharide residue maximizes the abundances of useful glycosidic bond and cross-ring cleavage ions, as highlighted by the rectangle on the figure. With more than one charge per residue, the abundances of ions produced from losses of the equivalent of $[H_2SO_4]^-$ occur with increasing abundances relative to glycosidic bond cleavages. For this process, the loss of a charged group evidently reduces excessive like-charge repulsions due to excessive density of charge. For synthetic heparins bearing four sulfate groups per GlcN residue, it is possible to produce an ion with 1.5 charge per monosaccharide residue that produces an abundant ion the *m/z* value of which is consistent with loss of $[H]^-$ from the precursor [149]. The fact that excessive like-charge repulsions favor fragmentation that are uninformative dictates that the number of charges per residue for HS oligosaccharide ions should be limited to between 0.75 and 1.25.

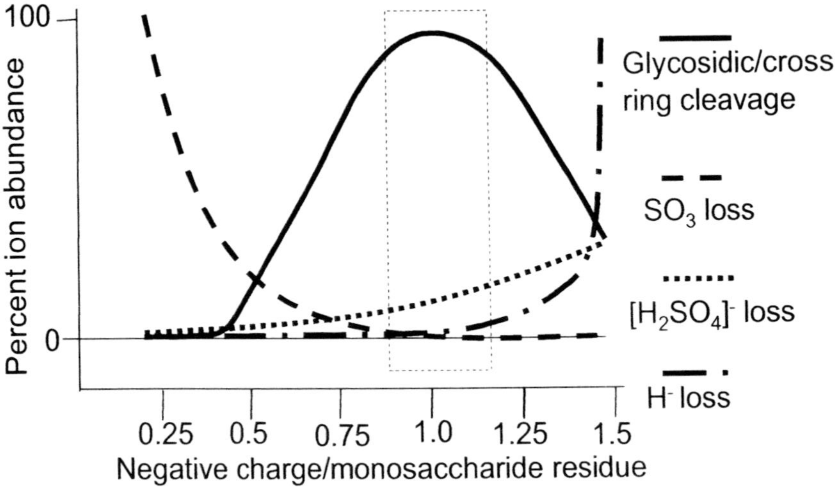

Figure 6. Trends in fragmentation types observed for HS oligosaccharides as a function of charge state. The plots are constructed from published HS/heparin tandem mass spectrometric data and represent general trends rather than exact product ion abundances. The rectangle highlights the region of precursor ion negative charge/residue observed to produce the most useful product ion patterns

8. LC/MS OF GAG OLIGOSACCHARIDES

The complexity of mixtures of oligosaccharides generated by enzymatic or chemical depolymerization of sulfated GAG chains precludes direct MS analysis without prior separation. Separation of CS/DS chains using high performance SEC provides sufficient separation to allow for direct MS analysis [139]. This mode of chromatography requires approximately 100 mM salt concentration to achieve adequate resolution and the use of ammonium acetate fulfills this requirement while not inhibiting mass spectrometric ion formation. SEC results in dilution of the GAG mixture, however, and the ammonium acetate salts will reduce signal strength to some degree. SEC may not, therefore, provide sufficient ion signal for the analysis of CS released from biological samples available in small supply (*i.e.* less than a few micrograms). On-line SEC/MS for separation and analysis of low molecular weight heparins using an ESI time-of-flight instrument has been used to determine the compositions of over 60 components in the GAG mixture [150]. In this work, the formation of heparin oligosaccharides using negative ESI resulted in ambiguous mass determinations, necessitating the removal of cations from the methanol/water/ammonium bicarbonate chromatographic solvent. The authors demonstrate that a commercially available self regenerating cation exchange column results in a 100-fold improvement in signal intensity and an increase in the negative ion charge state (in absolute terms). A chemical reaction mass spectrometric detector has been used to determine the elemental and isotopic composition of heparin preparations eluting from an SEC column [151, 152].

The use of basic peptides to pair polysulfated oligosaccharides has been used in ESI MS analysis in the positive mode. Cationic dyes have long been used in the analysis of sulfated GAGs both as a means of compound-class specific precipitation and as a means of spectrophotometric quantification. Taking advantage of this phenomenon, researchers have paired alkylammonium ions with polysulfated carbohydrates to enhance their hydrophobicity and thus facilitate reversed phase separations [153-155]. Tetrabutylammonium salts effectively pair with HS disaccharide digestion products, allowing reversed phase analysis [117, 119]. More recent research has identified dibutyl amine as an ion pairing agent compatible with on-line positive ion ESI LC/MS of heparin oligosaccharides [112]. Other researchers have used tributylammonium salts for this purpose [156]. Sulfated amines such as aminonaphthalenetrisulfonic acid, when used as reductive amination reagents, confer acidity on neutral glycans, thereby facilitating their analysis by electrophoresis [157] or capillary electrophoresis-MS [158] and triethylammonium salts have been used to pair such derivatized oligosaccharides for on-line LC/MS studies [159]. The use of ion pairs carries the advantage that it combines a high resolution reversed phase chromatographic separation with on-line mass spectrometric detection. It carries the disadvantage that the amines must be continuously pumped into the ion source.

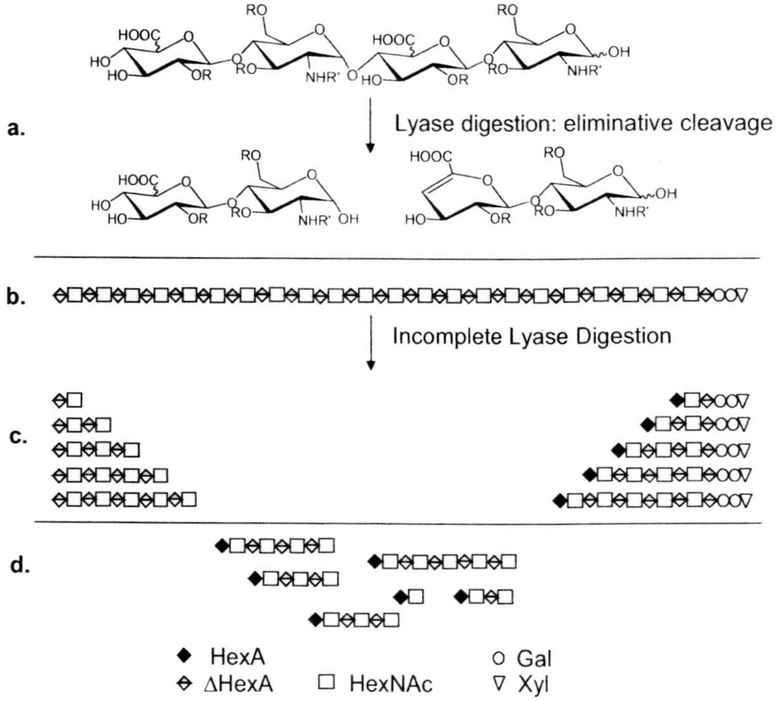

Figure 7. Lyase based sequence ladders of CS/DS and HS/heparin GAGs, (a) eliminative cleavage of a heparin tetramer, R = H or SO_3H, R' = H or SO_3H or Ac, resulting in the formation of a 4,5-unsaturated (Δ-unsaturated) uronic acid residue on the new non-reducing terminus, (b) a GAG chain (CS/DS or HS/heparin) is digested with a lyase enzyme using conditions to generate inclomplete extent of digestion to generate (c) products containing either the original reducing end (that include the linker structure) or the non-reducing end (that include a saturated uronic acid residue at their non-reducing ends) and (d) products from the interior of the original GAG chain with Δ-unsaturated HexA on the non-reducing ends and HexN on the reducing ends

Determination of the masses of HS oligosaccharides defines the compositions with respect to the numbers of HexA, HexN, sulfate and acetate groups. In addition, lyase digestion products containing the original reducing or non-reducing ends of the HS/heparin chain have unique mass values relative to other oligosaccharides in the mixture as shown in

Figure 7. Under partial lyase digestion conditions, a series of oligosaccharides will be detected using the on-line reversed phase ion pairing LC/MS approach. Some of these oligosaccharides will have mass values consistent with a saturated HexA residue at their non-reducing terminus. Figure 7c) that derives from the non-reducing end of the parent chain. Ions that contain the reducing end of the parent GAG will contain part of the linker oligosaccharide, depending on the method used to release the GAG from the core protein, and also have unique masses. The mass differences among the terminal series define the composition of each disaccharide in the sequence [156]. Other oligosaccharides will have mass values consistent with ΔHexA at the non-reducing terminus that result from lyase digestion to the interior of the GAG chainFigure 7d). Therefore, an on-line ion pairing LC/MS data set will contain information on the structure of the entire GAG chain, provided that an extended series of ions containing the reducing and non-reducing ends of the intact chain can be detected.

9. Capillary Electrophoresis/MS of GAG Oligosaccharides

Sulfated GAG di- and oligosaccharides produced by lyase digestion, by virtue of their acidity, migrate towards the anode in reversed polarity capillary electrophoresis (CE) and may be detected using the unique absorbance at 232 nm afforded by the Δ-unsaturated bond in the non-reducing terminal HexA residue [160]. The most highly sulfated oligosaccharides exhibit the fastest migration in the reversed polarity mode of CE, and the unsulfated molecules migrate slowly. In forward polarity CE, the electroosmotic flow suffices to carry sulfated GAG oligosaccharides toward the cathode despite their anionic nature and the most highly sulfated GAG oligosaccharides migrate the slowest [161, 162]. Because of the comparatively small path length in the capillary and the low volume of injection, the CE analysis requires at least 250 pmol of each disaccharide in a five microliter volume for detection of the Δ-unsaturated HexA residue at 232 nm. The addition of a chromophore or fluorophore via reductive amination dramatically reduces the detection limits for CE of GAG disaccharides, and derivatives appropriate for laser induced fluorescence detection produce impressive results [59, 60, 115].

The use of a sheathless interface for on-line CE/MS, first shown for separation of complex *O*-glycosylated peptide mixtures using ammonium acetate/ammonium hydroxide salts [163], allows screening of a several glycan classes [164]. Separation of CS/DS oligosaccharide mixtures using forward polarity CE with ammonium acetate buffer at pH 12.0 results in the detection of 10 peaks in a 10 minute electropherogram [140]. Subsequent negative ion nano ESI MS on a Q-TOF instrument reveals several different CS/DS compositions in a collected CE fraction and sufficient ion signal for tandem mass spectrometric analysis [136]. A similar approach has been used for off-line CE MS of ganglioside mixtures [137]. The extension of this work to on-line sheathless CE/MS of GAG oligosaccharides yielded impressive results in which CS/DS oligosaccharides with more sulfate groups than GalNAc residues, termed oversulfated oligosaccharides, were identified [135].

Mass spectrometric analysis of GAG oligosaccharides released from small tissue samples or from model organisms such as *Drosophila* or *C. elegans* requires miniaturization of the sample interface. As shown from the published work, CE provides a powerful means for both resolving and on-line introduction of the GAG oligosaccharide mixture into the mass spectrometer. It is unclear at this time, however, if CE/MS will be sensitive enough to enable analysis of sub-microgram quantities of GAGs released from small tissue samples.

10. APPLICATIONS TO MUCOPOLYSACCHARIDOSIS

Catabolism of proteoglycans occurs by an ordered process, culminating in the formation of monosaccharides in the lysosome. Proteolytic enzymes first degrade the core protein, followed by endoglycosidic cleavage of the GAG chains into large pieces. A series of exoglycosidases and sulfatases then remove residues from the non-reducing terminus of each GAG oligosaccharide until only monosaccharides remain. Because of the exolytic nature of the final steps of GAG degradation, the lack or misfunction of one exolytic enzyme causes the accumulation of partially degraded material in the lysosome, with deleterious health effects of varying severity. Mucopolysaccharidosis (MPS) is a class of lysosomal storage disorder [for a review see [165]] in which the lack of normal GAG-degrading enzyme activity results in accumulation of partially degraded oligosaccharides in the lysosome and elevated levels of GAG excretion into the urine relative to normal subjects. In general, subjects with the MPS diseases suffer from neurological and skeletal abnormalities and often do not live past young adulthood. Because therapies must commence as early in life as possible to minimize developmental abnormalities, effective analytical diagnostic and treatment-monitoring methods are needed. Treatment measures include enzyme replacement therapy [166, 167] and gene therapy [168]. A number of diagnostic approaches exist for characterizing MPS phenotypes, including electrophoretic patterning [35]. Mass spectrometric approaches to diagnosis of MPS phenotypes and for monitoring treatment have been developed [167, 169, 170].

The four types of Sanfilippo syndrome (mucopolysaccharidosis type III) arise from the lack of a HS/heparin degrading enzyme activity (type A, heparan *N*-sulfatase; type B, *N*-acetylglucosaminidase; type C, acetyl CoA: α-glucosaminideacetyltransferase; and type D, *N*-acetylglucosamine 6-sulfatase), each leading to similar clinical symptoms. Effective clinical treatment depends on identification of the deficient enzyme, presently carried out using radiometry [171], spectrophotometry [172], or fluorometry [173]. In an effort to measure all four enzyme activities on a single platform, an affinity mass spectrometry scheme has been developed to measure the four heparin degrading enzyme activities in cell lysates derived from forearm skin biopsies [174, 175]. The researchers synthesized enzymatic substrates conjugated to biotin and deuterated versions of the digestion products also conjugated to biotin. By adding both compounds to the lysates and allowing enzymatic digestion to occur, the biotin-conjugated substrate is converted to product of the same structure as the deuterated biotin-conjugated internal standard. Thus, mass spectra from normal level of enzymatic activity display deuterated and non-deuterated forms of the product and abnormal enzymatic activity results in the absence of the non-deuterated ion. The biotin handle carries the advantage that the activity measurement occurs in a complex lysate not directly compatible with mass spectrometry. The MS approach described combines measurement of all four enzymatic activities in a single platform.

Analysis of urine samples spiked with radiolabeled monosaccharides by ion exchange chromatography followed by paper chromatography established that sulfated hexosamine levels correlate with the types and severity of MPS diseases [176-178]. A recently described ESI mass spectrometric method quantifies mono- and disaccharides in urine samples of MPS patients with minimal sample workup, improving on existing methods [179]. Urine (or blood plasma) was lyophilized and derivatized using 1-phenyl-3-methyl pyrazolone (PMP) [180] and the excess reagent removed by solvent extraction. The aqueous layer was subjected to reversed phase chromatography and analyzed off-line using negative ESI MS. A deuterated, PMP-derivatized *N*-acetylglucosamine-6-sulfate standard was used as an internal control to quantitate the total monosulfated HexNAc levels, a combination of GalNAc4S, GalNAc6S, and GlcNAc6S. In addition, disulfated HexNAc and monosulfated HexNAc-HexA were quantified relative to the internal standard. The levels of these three ions (HexNAcS, $HexNAcS_2$ and HexNAcS-HexA) in urine effectively differentiated MPS patients from controls. This methodology has been used to monitor dose response of enzyme replacement therapy in feline MPS VI (*N*-acetylgalactosamine-4-sulfatase deficiency) [167]. In this work, the HexNAcS/HexNAcS-HexA ratio was significantly higher in urine of untreated MPS VI than in normal or treated animals.

Negative ESI MS of GAGs isolated from urine by a combination of anion exchange and gel filtration chromatography with subsequent PMP derivatization resulted in the identification of oligosaccharides the levels of which correlate with MPS type I (α-L-iduronidase deficiency) [169]. Tandem MS was used to characterize a tetrasaccharide, the levels of which were elevated in MPS I patient urine.

11. Conclusions

Determination of the mass of GAG oligosaccharides serves to define the composition with respect to monosaccharides residues, sulfate and acetate groups. The published record on MS of GAG oligosaccharides demonstrates effective use of MALDI of these molecules paired with basic peptides in the positive mode, ESI paired with basic peptides or other ammonium cations, and direct negative ESI to generate deprotonated ions. Any of these approaches may be used to determine the masses of GAG oligosaccharides before and after enzymatic or chemical digestion to reveal structural information or partial sequences. Tandem MS of positively charged GAG oligosaccharide ions typically results in abundant ions produced from fragmentation to the sulfate groups and loss of valuable information. Such analysis of ions with multiple negative charges, however, produce ion profiles with considerable structural value. The product ion patterns depend strongly on the ion charge state, and it is generally possible to observe abundant ions from glycosidic bond cleavages. While sulfated GAG oligosaccharides may be analyzed using either MALDI or ESI, only the latter technique produces ions amenable to tandem mass spectrometry.

12. References

[1] Mann, M., and Jensen, O. N. Proteomic analysis of post-translational modifications (2003) *Nat Biotechnol* 21, 255-61.

[2] Varki, A., Cummings, R., Esko, J., Freeze, H., Hart, G., and Marth, G. (1999) Essentials of Glycobiology, Cold Spring Harbor Laboratory Press, Cold Spring Harbor, NY.

[3] Wells, L., Whelan, S. A., and Hart, G. W. O-GlcNAc: a regulatory post-translational modification (2003) *Biochem Biophys Res Commun* 302, 435-41.

[4] Zachara, N. E., and Hart, G. W. O-GlcNAc a sensor of cellular state: the role of nucleocytoplasmic glycosylation in modulating cellular function in response to nutrition and stress (2004) *Biochim Biophys Acta* 1673, 13-28.

[5] Wells, L., and Hart, G. W. O-GlcNAc turns twenty: functional implications for post-translational modification of nuclear and cytosolic proteins with a sugar (2003) *FEBS Lett* 546, 154-8.

[6] Handa, S., and Nakamura, K. Modification of sialic acid carboxyl group of ganglioside (1984) *J Biochem (Tokyo)* 95, 1323-29.

[7] Powell, A. K., and Harvey, D. J. Stabilization of sialic acids in *N*-linked oligosaccharides and gangliosides for analysis by positive ion matrix-assisted laser desorption/ionization mass spectrometry (1996) *Rapid Commun Mass Spectrom* 10, 1027-32.

[8] Wong, A. W., Wang, H., and Lebrilla, C. B. Selection of anionic dopant for quantifying desialylation reactions with MALDI-FTMS (2000) *Anal Chem* 72, 1419-25.

[9] Wong, A. W., Cancilla, M. T., Voss, L. R., and Lebrilla, C. B. Anion dopant for oligosaccharides in matrix-assisted laser desorption/ionization mass spectrometry (1999) *Anal Chem* 71, 205-11.

[10] O'Connor, P. B., Mirgorodskaya, E., and Costello, C. E. High pressure matrix-assisted laser desorption/ionization Fourier transform mass spectrometry for minimization of ganglioside fragmentation (2002) *J Am Soc Mass Spectrom* 13, 402-07.

[11] O'Connor, P. B., and Costello, C. E. A high pressure matrix-assisted laser desorption/ionization Fourier transform mass spectrometry ion source for thermal stabilization of labile biomolecules (2001) *Rapid Commun Mass Spectrom* 15, 1862-68.

[12] Ernst, B., Müller, D. R., and Richter, W. J. False sugar sequence ions in electrospray tandem mass spectrometry of underivatized sialyl-Lewis-type oligosaccharides (1997) *Int J Mass Spectrom Ion Proc* 160, 283-90.

[13] Harvey, D. J., Mattu, T. S., Wormald, M. R., Royle, L., Dwek, R. A., and Rudd, P. M. "Internal residue loss": rearrangements occurring during the fragmentation of carbohydrates derivatized at the reducing terminus (2002) *Anal Chem* 74, 734-40.

[14] Zaia, J. Mass spectrometry of oligosaccharides (2004) *Mass Spectrom Rev* 23, 161-227.

[15] Tai, G. H., Nieduszynski, I. A., Fullwood, N. J., and Huckerby, T. N. Human corneal keratan sulfates (1997) *J Biol Chem* 272, 28227-31.

[16] Lauder, R. M., Huckerby, T. N., and Nieduszynski, I. A. The structure of the keratan sulphate chains attached to fibromodulin from human articular cartilage (1997) *Glycoconj J* 14, 651-60.

[17] Tai, G. H., Huckerby, T. N., and Nieduszynski, I. A. Multiple non-reducing chain termini isolated from bovine corneal keratan sulfates (1996) *J Biol Chem* 271, 23535-46.

[18] Whitham, K. M., Hadley, J. L., Morris, H. G., Andrew, S. M., Nieduszynski, I. A., and Brown, G. M. An improved method for the structural profiling of keratan sulfates:

analysis of keratan sulfates from brain and ovarian tumors (1999) *Glycobiology* 9, 285-91.

[19] Cheng, F., Heinegard, D., Malmstrom, A., Schmidtchen, A., Yoshida, K., and Fransson, L. A. Patterns of uronosyl epimerization and 4-/6-*O*-sulphation in chondroitin/dermatan sulphate from decorin and biglycan of various bovine tissues (1994) *Glycobiology* 4, 685-96.

[20] Venkataraman, G., Sasisekharan, V., Cooney, C. L., Langer, R., and Sasisekharan, R. A stereochemical approach to pyranose ring flexibility: its implications for the conformation of dermatan sulfate (1994) *Proc Natl Acad Sci U S A* 91, 6171-75.

[21] Lindahl, U., Kusche-Gullberg, M., and Kjellen, L. Regulated diversity of heparan sulfate (1998) *J Biol Chem* 273, 24979-82.

[22] Bernfield, M., Gotte, M., Park, P. W., Reizes, O., Fitzgerald, M. L., Lincecum, J., and Zako, M. Functions of cell surface heparan sulfate proteoglycans (1999) *Annu Rev Biochem* 68, 729-77.

[23] Esko, J. D., and Zhang, L. Influence of core protein sequence on glycosaminoglycan assembly (1996) *Curr Opin Struct Biol* 6, 663-70.

[24] Perrimon, N., and Bernfield, M. Specificities of heparan sulphate proteoglycans in developmental processes (2000) *Nature* 404, 725-8.

[25] Esko, J. D., and Lindahl, U. Molecular diversity of heparan sulfate (2001) *J Clin Invest* 108, 169-73.

[26] Conrad, H. E. (1998) Heparin Binding Proteins, Academic Press, New York.

[27] Lander, A. D. Proteoglycans: master regulators of molecular encounter? (1998) *Matrix Biol* 17, 465-72.

[28] Nugent, M. A., Nugent, H. M., Iozzo, R. V., Sanchack, K., and Edelman, E. R. Perlecan is required to inhibit thrombosis after deep vascular injury and contributes to endothelial cell-mediated inhibition of intimal hyperplasia (2000) *Proc Natl Acad Sci U S A* 97, 6722-7.

[29] Nybakken, K., and Perrimon, N. Heparan sulfate proteoglycan modulation of developmental signaling in Drosophila (2002) *Biochim Biophys Acta* 1573, 280-91.

[30] Mahoney, D. J., Aplin, R. T., Calabro, A., Hascall, V. C., and Day, A. J. Novel methods for the preparation and characterization of hyaluronan oligosaccharides of defined length (2001) *Glycobiology* 11, 1025-33.

[31] Roboz, J., Deng, L., Ma, L., and Silides, D. Monitoring the Stepwise Decomposition of Hyaluronan by Hyaluronidase in Pleural/Peritoneal Effusions from Patients with Malignant Mesothelioma Using Negative Electrospray Mass Spectrometry. (2000) *Proc 48th ASMS Conf Mass Spectrom Allied Topics.*

[32] Price, K. N., Al, T., Baker, D. C., Chisena, C., and Cysyk, R. L. Isolation and characterization by electrospray-ionization mass spectrometry and high-performance anion-exchange chromatography of oligosaccharides derived from hyaluronic acid by hyaluronate lyase digestion: observation of some heretofore unobserved oligosaccharides that contain an odd number of units (1997) *Carbohydr Res* 303, 303-11.

[33] Koketsu, M., and Linhardt, R. J. Electrophoresis for the analysis of acidic oligosaccharides (2000) *Anal Biochem* 283, 136-45.

[34] Mao, W. J., Thanawiroon, C., and Linhardt, R. J. Capillary electrophoresis for the analysis of glycosaminoglycans and glycosaminoglycan-derived oligosaccharides (2002) *Biomed Chromatogr* 16, 77-94.

[35] Byers, S., Rozaklis, T., Brumfield, L. K., Ranieri, E., and Hopwood, J. J. Glycosaminoglycan accumulation and excretion in the mucopolysaccharidoses: characterization and basis of a diagnostic test for MPS (1998) *Mol Genet Metab* 65, 282-90.

[36] 36. Maccari, F., and Volpi, N. Glycosaminoglycan blotting on nitrocellulose membranes treated with cetylpyridinium chloride after agarose-gel electrophoretic separation (2002) *Electrophoresis* 23, 3270-7.

[37] Horenberg, J., and De Vries, J. X. Characterization of heparinsby high-pressure size exclusion liquid chromatography (1983) *J Chrom* 261, 287-92.

[38] de Vries, J. X. Analysis of heparins by size-exclusion and reversed-phase high-performance liquid chromatography with photodiode-array detection (1989) *J Chromatogr* 465, 297-304.

[39] Kristensen, H. I., Tromborg, E. M., Nielsen, J. R., Nielsen, J. I., Johansen, K. B., and Ostergaard, P. B. Development and validation of a size exclusion chromatography method for determination of molecular masses and molecular mass distribution in low molecular weight heparin (1991) *Thromb Res* 64, 131-41.

[40] Maderich, A. B., and Sugita, E. T. Determination of polyanionic macromolecules by size-exclusion chromatography (1993) *J Chromatogr* 622, 278-83.

[41] Malsch, R., and Harenberg, J. High-performance size exclusion chromatography and polyacrylamide gel electrophoresis for characterization of unfractionated and low molecular mass glycosaminoglycans (1994) *Semin Thromb Hemost* 20, 135-43.

[42] Soltes, L., Mislovicova, D., and Sebille, B. Insight into the distribution of molecular weights and higher-order structure of hyaluronans and some beta-(1 --> 3)-glucans by size exclusion chromatography (1996) *Biomed Chromatogr* 10, 53-9.

[43] Knobloch, J. E., and Shaklee, P. N. Absolute molecular weight distribution of low-molecular-weight heparins by size-exclusion chromatography with multiangle laser light scattering detection (1997) *Anal Biochem* 245, 231-41.

[44] Volpi, N., and Bolognani, L. Glycosaminoglycans and proteins: different behaviours in high-performance size-exclusion chromatography (1993) *J Chromatogr* 630, 390-6.

[45] Guo, X., Condra, M., Kimura, K., Berth, G., Dautzenberg, H., and Dubin, P. L. Determination of molecular weight of heparin by size exclusion chromatography with universal calibration (2003) *Anal Biochem* 312, 33-9.

[46] Ernst, S., Langer, R., Cooney, C. L., and Sasisekharan, R. Enzymatic degradation of glycosaminoglycans (1995) *Crit Rev Biochem Mol Biol* 30, 387-444.

[47] Takagaki, K., Ishido, K., Kakizaki, I., Iwafune, M., and Endo, M. Carriers for enzymatic attachment of glycosaminoglycan chains to peptide (2002) *Biochem Biophys Res Commun* 293, 220-4.

[48] Takagaki, K., Munakata, H., Kakizaki, I., Iwafune, M., Itabashi, T., and Endo, M. Domain structure of chondroitin sulfate E octasaccharides binding to type V collagen (2002) *J Biol Chem* 277, 8882-9.

[49] Takagaki, K., Munakata, H., Majima, M., Kakizaki, I., and Endo, M. Chimeric glycosaminoglycan oligosaccharides synthesized by enzymatic reconstruction and their

use in substrate specificity determination of Streptococcus hyaluronidase (2000) *J Biochem (Tokyo)* 127, 695-702.

[50] Takagaki, K., Munakata, H., Majima, M., and Endo, M. Enzymatic reconstruction of a hybrid glycosaminoglycan containing 6- sulfated, 4-sulfated, and unsulfated *N*-acetylgalactosamine (1999) *Biochem Biophys Res Commun* 258, 741-4.

[51] Shively, J. E., and Conrad, H. E. Formation of anhydrosugars in the chemical depolymerization of heparin (1976) *Biochemistry* 15, 3932-42.

[52] Plaas, A. H., Wong-Palms, S., Roughley, P. J., Midura, R. J., and Hascall, V. C. Chemical and immunological assay of the nonreducing terminal residues of chondroitin sulfate from human aggrecan (1997) *J Biol Chem* 272, 20603-10.

[53] Plaas, A. H., Hascall, V. C., and Midura, R. J. Ion exchange HPLC microanalysis of chondroitin sulfate: quantitative derivatization of chondroitin lyase digestion products with 2- aminopyridine [published erratum appears in Glycobiology 1997 Sep;7(6):xiv] (1996) *Glycobiology* 6, 823-9.

[54] Calabro, A., Midura, R., Wang, A., West, L., Plaas, A., and Hascall, V. C. Fluorophore-assisted carbohydrate electrophoresis (FACE) of glycosaminoglycans (2001) *Osteoarthritis Cartilage* 9 Suppl A, S16-22.

[55] Calabro, A., Hascall, V. C., and Midura, R. J. Adaptation of FACE methodology for microanalysis of total hyaluronan and chondroitin sulfate composition from cartilage (2000) *Glycobiology* 10, 283-93.

[56] Calabro, A., Benavides, M., Tammi, M., Hascall, V. C., and Midura, R. J. Microanalysis of enzyme digests of hyaluronan and chondroitin/dermatan sulfate by fluorophore-assisted carbohydrate electrophoresis (FACE) (2000) *Glycobiology* 10, 273-81.

[57] Militsopoulou, M., Lamari, F., and Karamanos, N. K. Capillary electrophoresis: a tool for studying interactions of glycans/proteoglycans with growth factors (2003) *J Pharm Biomed Anal* 32, 823-28.

[58] Lamari, F. N., Kuhn, R., and Karamanos, N. K. Derivatization of carbohydrates for chromatographic, electrophoretic and mass spectrometric structure analysis (2003) *J Chromatogr B Analyt Technol Biomed Life Sci* 793, 15-36.

[59] Lamari, F. N., Militsopoulou, M., Mitropoulou, T. N., Hjerpe, A., and Karamanos, N. K. Analysis of glycosaminoglycan-derived disaccharides in biologic: samples by capillary electrophoresis and protocol for sequencing glycosaminoglycans (2002) *Biomed Chromatogr* 16, 95-102.

[60] Militsopoulou, M., Lamari, F. N., Hjerpe, A., and Karamanos, N. K. Determination of twelve heparin- and heparan sulfate-derived disaccharides as 2-aminoacridone derivatives by capillary zone electrophoresis using ultraviolet and laser-induced fluorescence detection (2002) *Electrophoresis* 23, 1104-9.

[61] Stringer, S. E., Kandola, B. S., Pye, D. A., and Gallagher, J. T. Heparin sequencing (2003) *Glycobiology* 13, 97-107.

[62] Turnbull, J., Powell, A., and Guimond, S. Heparan sulfate: decoding a dynamic multifunctional cell regulator (2001) *Trends Cell Biol* 11, 75-82.

[63] Drummond, K. J., Yates, E. A., and Turnbull, J. E. Electrophoretic sequencing of heparin/heparan sulfate oligosaccharides using a highly sensitive fluorescent end label (2001) *Proteomics* 1, 304-10.

[64] Turnbull, J. E., Hopwood, J. J., and Gallagher, J. T. A strategy for rapid sequencing of heparan sulfate and heparin saccharides (1999) *Proc Natl Acad Sci U S A* 96, 2698-703.

[65] Geyer, H., Bahr, U., Liedtke, S., Schachner, M., and Geyer, R. Core structures of polysialylated glycans present in neural cell adhesion molecule from newborn mouse brain (2001) *Eur J Biochem* 268, 6587-99.

[66] Wheeler, S. F., and Harvey, D. J. Extension of the In-Gel Release Method for Structural Analysis of Neutral and Sialylated *N*-Linked Glycans to the Analysis of Sulfated Glycans: Application to the Glycans from Bovine Thyroid-Stimulating Hormone (2001) *Anal Biochem* 296, 96-100.

[67] Karlsson, N. G., Johansson, M. E., Asker, N., Karlsson, H., Gendler, S. J., Carlstedt, I., and Hansson, G. C. Molecular characterization of the large heavily glycosylated domain glycopeptide from the rat small intestinal Muc2 mucin (1996) *Glycoconj J* 13, 823-31.

[68] Karlsson, N. G., Karlsson, H., and Hansson, G. C. Sulphated mucin oligosaccharides from porcine small intestine analysed by four-sector tandem mass spectrometry (1996) *J Mass Spectrom* 31, 560-72.

[69] Thomsson, K. A., Karlsson, N. G., and Hansson, G. C. Liquid chromatography-electrospray mass spectrometry as a tool for the analysis of sulfated oligosaccharides from mucin glycoproteins (1999) *J Chromatogr A* 854, 131-9.

[70] Thomsson, K. A., Karlsson, H., and Hansson, G. Sequencing sulfated oligosaccharides from mucins by liquid chromatography and electrospray ionization tandem mass spectrometry (2000) *Anal Chem* 72, 4543-49.

[71] Robbe, C., Capon, C., Coddeville, B., and Michalski, J. C. Diagnostic ions for the rapid analysis by nano-electrospray ionization quadrupole time-of-flight mass spectrometry of O-glycans from human mucins (2004) *Rapid Commun Mass Spectrom* 18, 412-20.

[72] Juhasz, P., and Biemann, K. Utility of non-covalent complexes in the matrix-assisted laser desorption ionization mass spectrometry of heparin-derived oligosaccharides (1995) *Carbohydr Res* 270, 131-47.

[73] Juhasz, P., and Biemann, K. Mass spectrometric molecular-weight determination of highly acidic compounds of biological significance via their complexes with basic polypeptides (1994) *Proc Natl Acad Sci U S A* 91, 4333-37.

[74] Reinhold, V. N., Carr, S. A., Green, B. N., Petitou, M., Choay, J., and Sinay, P. Structural characterization of sulfated glycosaminoglycans by fast atom bombardment mass spectrometry: application to heparin fragments prepared by chemical synthesis (1987) *Carbohydr Res* 161, 305-13.

[75] Ii, T., Okuda, S., Hirano, T., and Ohashi, M. Tandem mass spectrometry for characterization of unsaturated disaccharides from chondroitin sulfate, dermatan sulfate and hyaluronan (1994) *Glycoconj J* 11, 123-32.

[76] Ii, T., Kubota, M., Hirano, T., Ohashi, M., Yoshida, K., and Suzuki, S. FAB CID-MS/MS characterization of tetrasaccharide tri- and tetrasulfate derived from the antigenic determinant recognized by the anti- chondroitin sulfate monoclonal antibody MO-225 (1995) *Glycoconj J* 12, 282-89.

[77] Khoo, K. H., Morris, H. R., McDowell, R. A., Dell, A., Maccarana, M., and Lindahl, U. FABMS/derivatisation strategies for the analysis of heparin-derived oligosaccharides (1993) *Carbohydr Res* 244, 205-23.

[78] Chai, W., Rosankiewicz, J. R., and Lawson, A. M. TLC-LSIMS of neoglycolipids of glycosaminoglycan disaccharides and of oxymercuration cleavage products of heparin fragments that contain unsaturated uronic acid (1995) *Carbohydr Res* 269, 111-24.

[79] Sugahara, K., Takemura, Y., Sugiura, M., Kohno, Y., Yoshida, K., Takeda, K., Khoo, K. H., Morris, H. R., and Dell, A. Chondroitinase ABC-resistant sulfated trisaccharides isolated from digests of chondroitin/dermatan sulfate chains (1994) *Carbohydr Res* 255, 165-82.

[80] Carr, S. A., and Reinhold, V. N. Structural characterization of sulfated glycosaminoglycans by fast atom bombardment mass spectrometry: application to chondroitin sulfate (1984) *J Carbohydr Chem* 3, 381-401.

[81] Ciucanu, I., and Kerek, F. A simple and rapid method for the permethylation of carbohydrates (1984) *Carbohydr Res* 131, 209-17.

[82] McNeil, M., Darvill, A. G., Aman, P., Franzen, L. E., and Albersheim, P. Structural analysis of complex carbohydrates using high-performance liquid chromatography, gas chromatography, and mass spectrometry (1982) *Methods Enzymol* 83, 3-45.

[83] Dell, A., Oates, J. E., Morris, H. R., and Egge, H. Structure determination of carbohydrates and glycosphingolipids by fast atom bombardment mass spectrometry (1983) *Int J Mass Spectrom Ion Phys* 46, 415-18.

[84] Dell, A., Morris, H. R., Egge, H., von Nicolai, H., and Strecker, G. Fast-atom bombardment mass spectrometry for carbohydrate structure determination (1983) *Carbohydr Res* 115, 41-52.

[85] Spengler, B., Kirsch, D., and Kaufmann, R. Metastable decay of peptides and proteins in matrix-assisted laser-desorption mass-spectrometry (1991) *Rapid Commun Mass Spectrom* 5, 198-202.

[86] Yu, W., Vath, J. E., Huberty, M. C., and Martin, S. A. Identification of the facile gas-phase cleavage of the Asp-Pro and Asp- Xxx peptide bonds in matrix-assisted laser desorption time-of-flight mass spectrometry (1993) *Anal Chem* 65, 3015-23.

[87] Spengler, B., Kirsch, D., Kaufmann, R., and Lemoine, J. Structure-Analysis of Branched Oligosaccharides Using Post-Source Decay in Matrix-Assisted Laser-Desorption Ionization Mass-Spectrometry (1994) *Organic Mass Spectrometry* 29, 782-87.

[88] Harvey, D. J. Matrix-assisted laser desorption/ionization mass spectrometry of carbohydrates and glycoconjugates (2003) *Mass Spectrom Rev* 226, 1-35.

[89] Harvey, D. J. Matrix-assisted laser desorption/ionization mass spectrometry of carbohydrates and glycoconjugates (2003) *International Journal of Mass Spectrometry* 226, 1-35.

[90] Vercruysse, K. P., Ziebell, M. R., and Prestwich, G. D. Control of enzymatic degradation of hyaluronan by divalent cations (1999) *Carbohydr Res* 318, 26-37.

[91] Schiller, J., Arnhold, J., Benard, S., Reichl, S., and Arnold, K. Cartilage degradation by hyaluronate lyase and chondroitin ABC lyase: a MALDI-TOF mass spectrometric study (1999) *Carbohydr Res* 318, 116-22.

[92] Courel, M. N., Maingonnat, C., Tranchepain, F., Deschrevel, B., Vincent, J. C., Bertrand, P., and Delpech, B. Importance of hyaluronan length in a hyaladherin-based assay for hyaluronan (2002) *Anal Biochem* 302, 285-90.

[93] Yeung, B., and Marecak, D. Molecular weight determination of hyaluronic acid by gel filtration chromatography coupled to matrix-assisted laser desorption ionization mass spectrometry (1999) *J Chromatogr A* 852, 573-81.

[94] Seyfried, N. T., Blundell, C. D., Day, A. J., and Almond, A. Preparation and application of biologically active fluorescent hyaluronan oligosaccharides (2004) *Glycobiology*.

[95] Mikami, T., Mizumoto, S., Kago, N., Kitagawa, H., and Sugahara, K. Specificities of three distinct human chondroitin/dermatan N-acetylgalactosamine 4-O-sulfotransferases demonstrated using partially desulfated dermatan sulfate as an acceptor: implication of differential roles in dermatan sulfate biosynthesis (2003) *J Biol Chem* 278, 36115-27.

[96] Ueoka, C., Nadanaka, S., Seno, N., Khoo, K. H., and Sugahara, K. Structural determination of novel tetra- and hexasaccharide sequences isolated from chondroitin sulfate H (oversulfated dermatan sulfate) of hagfish notochord (1999) *Glycoconj J* 16, 291-305.

[97] Venkataraman, G., Shriver, Z., Raman, R., and Sasisekharan, R. Sequencing complex polysaccharides (1999) *Science* 286, 537-42.

[98] Ernst, S., Rhomberg, A. J., Biemann, K., and Sasisekharan, R. Direct evidence for a predominantly exolytic processive mechanism for depolymerization of heparin-like glycosaminoglycans by heparinase I (1998) *Proc Natl Acad Sci U S A* 95, 4182-87.

[99] Rhomberg, A. J., Ernst, S., Sasisekharan, R., and Biemann, K. Mass spectrometric and capillary electrophoretic investigation of the enzymatic degradation of heparin-like glycosaminoglycans (1998) *Proc Natl Acad Sci U S A* 95, 4176-81.

[100] Rhomberg, A. J., Shriver, Z., Biemann, K., and Sasisekharan, R. Mass spectrometric evidence for the enzymatic mechanism of the depolymerization of heparin-like glycosaminoglycans by heparinase II (1998) *Proc Natl Acad Sci U S A* 95, 12232-37.

[101] Fromm, J. R., Hileman, R. E., Weiler, J. M., and Linhardt, R. J. Interaction of fibroblast growth factor-1 and related peptides with heparan sulfate and its oligosaccharides (1997) *Arch Biochem Biophys* 346, 252-62.

[102] Venkataraman, G., Shriver, Z., Davis, J. C., and Sasisekharan, R. Fibroblast growth factors 1 and 2 are distinct in oligomerization in the presence of heparin-like glycosaminoglycans (1999) *Proc Natl Acad Sci U S A* 96, 1892-97.

[103] Sturiale, L., Naggi, A., and Torri, G. MALDI mass spectrometry as a tool for characterizing glycosaminoglycan oligosaccharides and their interaction with proteins (2001) *Semin Thromb Hemost* 27, 465-72.

[104] Kreuger, J., Salmivirta, M., Sturiale, L., Gimenez-Gallego, G., and Lindahl, U. Sequence analysis of heparan sulfate epitopes with graded affinities for fibroblast growth factors 1 and 2 (2001) *J Biol Chem* 276, 30744-52.

[105] Guerrini, M., Agulles, T., Bisio, A., Hricovini, M., Lay, L., Naggi, A., Poletti, L., Sturiale, L., Torri, G., and Casu, B. Minimal heparin/heparan sulfate sequences for binding to fibroblast growth factor-1 (2002) *Biochem Biophys Res Commun* 292, 222-30.

[106] Prebyl, B. S., Kaczmarek, C., Tuinman, A. A., and Baker, D. C. Characterizing the electrospray-ionization mass spectral fragmentation pattern of enzymatically derived hyaluronic acid oligomers (2003) *Carbohydr Res* 338, 1381-7.

[107] Kuhn, A. V., Raith, K., Sauerland, V., and Neubert, R. H. Quantification of hyaluronic acid fragments in pharmaceutical formulations using LC-ESI-MS (2003) *J Pharm Biomed Anal* 30, 1531-7.

[108] Desaire, H., and Leary, J. Detection and quantification of the sulfated disaccharides in chondoritin sulfate by electrospray tandem mass spectrometry (2000) *J Am Soc Mass Spectrom* 11, 916-20.

[109] Chai, W., Luo, J., Lim, C. K., and Lawson, A. M. Characterization of heparin oligosaccharide mixtures as ammonium salts using electrospray mass spectrometry (1998) *Anal Chem* 70, 2060-6.

[110] Kim, Y. S., Ahn, M. Y., Wu, S. J., Kim, D. H., Toida, T., Teesch, L. M., Park, Y., Yu, G., Lin, J., and Linhardt, R. J. Determination of the structure of oligosaccharides prepared from acharan sulfate (1998) *Glycobiology* 8, 869-77.

[111] Gunay, N. S., Tadano-Aritomi, K., Toida, T., Ishizuka, I., and Linhardt, R. Evaluation of Counterions for Electrospray Ionization Mass Spectral Analysis of A Highly Sulfated Carbohydrate, Sucrose Octasulfate (2003) *Anal Chem* 75, 3226-31.

[112] Kuberan, B., Lech, M., Zhang, L., Wu, Z. L., Beeler, D. L., and Rosenberg, R. Analysis of Heparan Sulfate Oligosaccharides with Ion Pair-Reverse Phase Capillary High Performance Liquid Chromatography-Microelectrospray Ionization Time-of-Flight Mass Spectrometry (2002) *J Am Chem Soc* 124, 8707-18.

[113] Thanawiroon, C., and Linhardt, R. J. Separation of a complex mixture of heparin-derived oligosaccharides using reversed-phase high-performance liquid chromatography (2003) *J Chromatogr A* 1014, 215-23.

[114] Imanari, T., Toida, T., Koshiishi, I., and Toyoda, H. High-performance liquid chromatographic analysis of glycosaminoglycan- derived oligosaccharides (1996) *J Chromatogr A* 720, 275-93.

[115] Militsopoulou, M., Lecomte, C., Bayle, C., Couderc, F., and Karamanos, N. K. Laser-induced fluorescence as a powerful detection tool for capillary electrophoretic analysis of heparin/heparan sulfate disaccharides (2003) *Biomed Chromatogr* 17, 39-41.

[116] Toyoda, H., Nagashima, T., Hirata, R., Toida, T., and Imanari, T. Sensitive high-performance liquid chromatographic method with fluorometric detection for the determination of heparin and heparan sulfate in biological samples: application to human urinary heparan sulfate (1997) *J Chromatogr B Biomed Sci Appl* 704, 19-24.

[117] Toyoda, H., Yamamoto, H., Ogino, N., Toida, T., and Imanari, T. Rapid and sensitive analysis of disaccharide composition in heparin and heparan sulfate by reversed-phase ion-pair chromatography on a 2 um porous silica gel column (1999) *Journal of Chromatography A* 830, 197-201.

[118] Toyoda, H., Kinoshita-Toyoda, A., Fox, B., and Selleck, S. B. Structural analysis of glycosaminoglycans in animals bearing mutations in sugarless, sulfateless, and tout-velu. Drosophila homologues of vertebrate genes encoding glycosaminoglycan biosynthetic enzymes (2000) *J Biol Chem* 275, 21856-61.

[119] Toyoda, H., Kinoshita-Toyoda, A., and Selleck, S. B. Structural analysis of glycosaminoglycans in *Drosophila* and *Caenorhabditis elegans* and demonstration that tout-velu, a Drosophila gene related to EXT tumor suppressors, affects heparan sulfate in vivo (2000) *J Biol Chem* 275, 2269-75.

[120] Sudo, M., Sato, K., Chaidedgumjorn, A., Toyoda, H., Toida, T., and Imanari, T. (1)H nuclear magnetic resonance spectroscopic analysis for determination of glucuronic and iduronic acids in dermatan sulfate, heparin, and heparan sulfate (2001) *Anal Biochem* 297, 42-51.

[121] Sakai, S., Onose, J., Nakamura, H., Toyoda, H., Toida, T., Imanari, T., and Linhardt, R. J. Pretreatment procedure for the microdetermination of chondroitin sulfate in plasma and urine (2002) *Anal Biochem* 302, 169-74.

[122] Barth, H., Schafer, C., Adah, M. I., Zhang, F., Linhardt, R. J., Toyoda, H., Kinoshita-Toyoda, A., Toida, T., Van Kuppevelt, T. H., Depla, E., Von Weizsacker, F., Blum, H. E., and Baumert, T. F. Cellular binding of hepatitis C virus envelope glycoprotein E2 requires cell surface heparan sulfate (2003) *J Biol Chem* 278, 41003-12.

[123] Roboz, J. (1968) Introduction to Mass Spectrometry: Instrumentation and Techniques, Interscience, New York.

[124] Desaire, H., and Leary, J. A. Multicomponent quantification of diastereomeric hexosamine monosaccharides using ion trap tandem mass spectrometry (1999) *Anal Chem* 71, 4142-47.

[125] Desaire, H., Sirich, T. L., and Leary, J. A. Evidence of block and randomly sequenced chondroitin polysaccharides: sequential enzymatic digestion and quantification using ion trap tandem mass spectrometry (2001) *Anal Chem* 73, 3513-20.

[126] Saad, O. M., and Leary, J. A. Compositional analysis and quantification of heparin and heparan sulfate by electrospray ionization ion trap mass spectrometry (2003) *Anal Chem* 75, 2985-95.

[127] Linhardt, R. J., Wang, H. M., Loganthan, D., Lamb, D. J., and Mallis, L. M. Analysis of glycosaminoglycan-derived oligosaccharides using fast atom bombardment mass spectrometry (1992) *Carbohydr Res* 225, 137-45.

[128] Lawrence, R., Kuberan, B., Lech, M., Beeler, D. L., and Rosenberg, R. D. Mapping critical biological motifs and biosynthetic pathways of heparan sulfate (2004) *Glycobiology* 14, 467-79.

[129] Staatz, W. D., Toyoda, H., Kinoshita-Toyoda, A., Chhor, K., and Selleck, S. B. Analysis of proteoglycans and glycosaminoglycans from Drosophila (2001) *Methods Mol Biol* 171, 41-52.

[130] Mallis, L. M., Wang, H. M., Loganathan, D., and Linhardt, R. J. Sequence analysis of highly sulfated, heparin-derived oligosaccharides using fast atom bombardment mass spectrometry (1989) *Anal Chem* 61, 1453-58.

[131] Lamb, D. J., Wang, H. M., Mallis, L. M., and Linhardt, R. J. Negative ion fast-atom bombardment tandem mass spectrometry to determine sulfate and linkage position in glycosaminoglycan derived disaccharides (1992) *J Am Soc Mass Spectrom* 3, 797-803.

[132] McClellan, J. M., Costello, C. E., O'Connor, P. B., and Zaia, J. Influence of charge state on product ion mass spectra and the determination of 4S/6S sulfation sequence of chondroitin sulfate oligosaccharides (2002) *Anal Chem* 74, 3760-71.

[133] Egge, H., Dell, A., and Von Nicolai, H. Fucose containing oligosaccharides from human milk. I. Separation and identification of new constituents (1983) *Arch Biochem Biophys* 224, 235-53.

[134] Zaia, J., Li, X.-Q., Chan, S.-Y., and Costello, C. E. Tandem mass spectrometric strategies for determination of sulfation positions and uronic acid epimerization in chondroitin sulfate oligosaccharides. (2003) *J Am Soc Mass Spectrom* 14, 1270-81.

[135] Zamfir, A., Seidler, D. G., Schonherr, E., Kresse, H., and Peter-Katalinic, J. On-line sheathless capillary electrophoresis/nanoelectrospray ionization-tandem mass spectrometry for the analysis of glycosaminoglycan oligosaccharides (2004) *Electrophoresis* 25, 2010-6.

[136] Zamfir, A., Seidler, D. G., Kresse, H., and Peter-Katalinic, J. Structural investigation of chondroitin/dermatan sulfate oligosaccharides from human skin fibroblast decorin (2003) *Glycobiology*.
[137] Zamfir, A., Vukelic, Z., and Peter-Katalinic, J. A capillary electrophoresis and off-line capillary electrophoresis/electrospray ionization-quadrupole time of flight-tandem mass spectrometry approach for ganglioside analysis (2002) *Electrophoresis* 23, 2894-903.
[138] Zaia, J., McClellan, J. E., and Costello, C. E. Tandem mass spectrometric determination of the 4S/6S sulfation sequence in chondroitin sulfate oligosaccharides (2001) *Anal Chem* 73, 6030-39.
[139] Zaia, J., and Costello, C. E. Compositional analysis of glycosaminoglycans by electrospray mass spectrometry (2001) *Anal Chem* 73, 233-39.
[140] Zamfir, A., Seidler, D. G., Kresse, H., and Peter-Katalinc, J. Structural characterization of chondroitin/dermatan sulfate oligosaccharides from bovine aorta by capillary electrophoresis and electrospray ionization quadrupole time-of-flight tandem mass spectrometry (2002) *Rapid Commun Mass Spectrom* 16, 2015-24.
[141] Spengler, B., Dolce, J. W., and Cotter, R. J. Infrared-Laser Desorption Mass-Spectrometry of Oligosaccharides - Fragmentation Mechanisms and Isomer Analysis (1990) *Anal Chem* 62, 1731-37.
[142] Harvey, D. J. Matrix-assisted laser desorption/ionization mass spectrometry of carbohydrates (1999) *Mass Spectrom Rev* 18, 349-450.
[143] Carroll, J., Willard, D., and Lebrilla, C. Energetics of cross-ring cleavages and their relevance to the linkage determination of oligosaccharides (1995) *Analytica Chimica Acta* 307, 431-47.
[144] Saad, O. M., and Leary, J. A. Delineating mechanisms of dissociation for isomeric heparin disaccharides using isotope labeling and ion trap tandem mass spectrometry (2004) *J Am Soc Mass Spectrom* 15, 1274-86.
[145] Oguma, T., Toyoda, H., Toida, T., and Imanari, T. Analytical Method for Keratan Sulfates by High-Performance Liquid Chromatography/Turbo-Ionspray Tandem Mass Spectrometry (2001) *Anal Biochem* 290, 68-73.
[146] Kubota, M., Yoshida, K., Tawada, A., and Ohashi, M. Characterization of oligosaccharides of the lactosamine series derived from keratan sulfates by tandem mass spectrometry (2000) *Eu J Mass Spectrom* 6, 193-203.
[147] Miller, M. J., Qian, J., Seward, R., Li, X., Costello, C. E., and Zaia, J. Evaluation of multistage MS for determination of individual sulfation sites on chondroitin sulfate and keratan sulfate oligosaccharides (2003) *Proc 51st ASMS Conf on Mass Spectrom Allied Topics*.
[148] Zaia, J., and Costello, C. E. Tandem mass spectrometry of sulfated heparin-like glycosaminoglycan oligosaccharides (2003) *Anal Chem* 75, 2445-55.
[149] Naggar, E., Costello, C. E., and Zaia, J. Competing fragmentation processes in tandem mass spectra of heparin-like glycosaminoglycans (2004) *J Am Soc Mass Spectrom* 15, 1534-44.
[150] Henriksen, J., Ringborg, L. H., and Roepstorrf, P. On-line size-exclusion chromatography/mass spectrometry of low molecular mass heparin (2004) *J Mass Spectrom* 39, 1305-12.
[151] Lecchi, P., and Abramson, F. P. Analysis of biopolymers by size-exclusion chromatography-mass spectrometry (1998) *J Chromatogr A* 828, 509-13.

[152] Lecchi, P., and Abramson, F. P. Size exclusion chromatography-chemical reaction interface mass spectrometry: "a perfect match" (1999) *Anal Chem* 71, 2951-5.

[153] Guo, Y. C., and Conrad, H. E. Analysis of oligosaccharides from heparin by reversed-phase ion-pairing high-performance liquid chromatography (1988) *Anal Biochem* 168, 54-62.

[154] Karamanos, N. K., Vanky, P., Tzanakakis, G. N., Tsegenidis, T., and Hjerpe, A. Ion-pair high-performance liquid chromatography for determining disaccharide composition in heparin and heparan sulphate (1997) *J Chromatogr A* 765, 169-79.

[155] Linhardt, R. J., Gu, K. N., Loganathan, D., and Carter, S. R. Analysis of glycosaminoglycan-derived oligosaccharides using reversed-phase ion-pairing and ion-exchange chromatography with suppressed conductivity detection (1989) *Anal Biochem* 181, 288-96.

[156] Thanawiroon, C., Rice, K. G., Toida, T., and Linhardt, R. J. LC/MS sequencing approach for highly sulfated heparin-derived oligosaccharides (2004) *J Biol Chem* 279, 2608-15.

[157] Jackson, P. The use of polyacrylamide-gel electrophoresis for the high-resolution separation of reducing saccharides labelled with the fluorophore 8-aminonaphthalene-1,3,6-trisulphonic acid. Detection of picomolar quantities by an imaging system based on a cooled charge-coupled device (1990) *Biochem J* 270, 705-13.

[158] Gennaro, L. A., Delaney, J., Vouros, P., Harvey, D. J., and Domon, B. Capillary electrophoresis/electrospray ion trap mass spectrometry for the analysis of negatively charged derivatized and underivatized glycans (2002) *Rapid Commun Mass Spectrom* 16, 192-200.

[159] Gennaro, L. A., Harvey, D. J., and Vouros, P. Reversed-phase ion-pairing liquid chromatography/ion trap mass spectrometry for the analysis of negatively charged, derivatized glycans (2003) *Rapid Commun Mass Spectrom* 17, 1528-34.

[160] Pervin, A., al-Hakim, A., and Linhardt, R. J. Separation of glycosaminoglycan-derived oligosaccharides by capillary electrophoresis using reverse polarity (1994) *Anal Biochem* 221, 182-8.

[161] Ampofo, S. A., Wang, H. M., and Linhardt, R. J. Disaccharide compositional analysis of heparin and heparan sulfate using capillary zone electrophoresis (1991) *Anal Biochem* 199, 249-55.

[162] al-Hakim, A., and Linhardt, R. J. Capillary electrophoresis for the analysis of chondroitin sulfate- and dermatan sulfate-derived disaccharides (1991) *Anal Biochem* 195, 68-73.

[163] Zamfir, A., and Peter-Katalinic, J. Glycoscreening by on-line sheathless capillary electrophoresis/electrospray ionization-quadrupole time of flight-tandem mass spectrometry (2001) *Electrophoresis* 22, 2448-57.

[164] Zamfir, A., and Peter-Katalinic, J. Capillary electrophoresis-mass spectrometry for glycoscreening in biomedical research (2004) *Electrophoresis* 25, 1949-63.

[165] Meikle, P. J., Hopwood, J. J., Clague, A. E., and Carey, W. F. Prevalence of lysosomal storage disorders (1999) *JAMA* 281, 249-54.

[166] Wraith, J. E. Enzyme replacement therapy in mucopolysaccharidosis type I: progress and emerging difficulties (2001) *J Inherit Metab Dis* 24, 245-50.

[167] Crawley, A., Ramsay, S. L., Byers, S., Hopwood, J., and Meikle, P. J. Monitoring dose response of enzyme replacement therapy in feline mucopolysaccharidosis type VI by tandem mass spectrometry (2004) *Pediatr Res* 55, 585-91.

[168] Bosch, A., and Heard, J. M. Gene therapy for mucopolysaccharidosis (2003) *Int Rev Neurobiol* 55, 271-96.

[169] Fuller, M., Meikle, P. J., and Hopwood, J. J. Glycosaminoglycan degradation fragments in mucopolysaccharidosis I (2004) *Glycobiology* 14, 443-50.

[170] Meikle, P. J., Fuller, M., and Hopwood, J. J. Mass spectrometry in the study of lysosomal storage disorders (2003) *Cell Mol Biol (Noisy-le-grand)* 49, 769-77.

[171] Reynertson, R., Campbell, P., Ford, J. D., Jacobsson, I., Roden, L., and Thompson, J. N. New oligosaccharides from heparin and heparan sulfate and their use as substrates for heparin-degrading enzymes (1983) *J Biol Chem* 258, 7449-59.

[172] Nowakowski, R. W., Thompson, J. N., and Taylor, K. B. Sanfilippo syndrome, type D: a spectrophotometric assay with prenatal diagnostic potential (1989) *Pediatr Res* 26, 462-6.

[173] Marsh, J., and Fensom, A. H. 4-Methylumbelliferyl alpha-N-acetylglucosaminidase activity for diagnosis of Sanfilippo B disease (1985) *Clin Genet* 27, 258-62.

[174] Gerber, S. A., Turecek, F., and Gelb, M. H. Design and synthesis of substrate and internal standard conjugates for profiling enzyme activity in the Sanfilippo syndrome by affinity chromatography/electrospray ionization mass spectrometry (2001) *Bioconjug Chem* 12, 603-15.

[175] Gerber, S. A., Scott, C. R., Turecek, F., and Gelb, M. H. Direct profiling of multiple enzyme activities in human cell lysates by affinity chromatography/electrospray ionization mass spectrometry: application to clinical enzymology (2001) *Anal Chem* 73, 1651-7.

[176] Hopwood, J. J., and Elliott, H. Urinary excretion of sulphated N-acetylhexosamines in patients with various mucopolysaccharidoses (1985) *Biochem J* 229, 579-86.

[177] Hopwood, J. J., and Elliott, H. Isolation and characterization of N-acetylglucosamine 6-sulfate from the urine of a patient with Sanfilippo type D syndrome and its occurrence in normal urine (1983) *Biochem Int* 6, 831-6.

[178] Hopwood, J. J., and Elliott, H. N-acetylglucosamine 6-sulfate residues in keratan sulfate and heparan sulfate are desulfated by the same enzyme (1983) *Biochem Int* 6, 141-8.

[179] Ramsay, S. L., Meikle, P. J., and Hopwood, J. J. Determination of monosaccharides and disaccharides in mucopolysaccharidoses patients by electrospray ionisation mass spectrometry (2003) *Mol Genet Metab* 78, 193-204.

[180] Honda, S., Akao, E., Suzuki, S., Okuda, M., Kakehi, K., and Nakamura, J. High-Performance Liquid-Chromatography of Reducing Carbohydrates as Strongly Ultraviolet-Absorbing and Electrochemically Sensitive 1-Phenyl-3-Methyl-5-Pyrazolone Derivatives (1989) *Anal Biochem* 180, 351-57.

In: Principles of Biomacromolecular Mass Spectrometry
Editor: Simone Koenig, pp. 37-53
ISBN 1-60021-063-5

Chapter 2

FOURIER TRANSFORM ION CYCLOTRON RESONANCE MASS SPECTROMETRY FOR PROTEIN STRUCTURE ANALYSIS

Christian Ihling and Andrea Sinz*
Biotechnological-Biomedical Center, Faculty of Chemistry and Mineralogy,
University of Leipzig, D-04103 Leipzig, Germany

ABSTRACT

FTICR (Fourier transform ion cyclotron resonance) mass spectrometry offers several advantages for the analysis of biological samples, including excellent mass resolution, ultra-high mass accuracy, and a wide mass range. This paper gives a short overview of recent applications and technological developments of FTICRMS, which are relevant to the field of protein analysis. Tandem mass spectrometry, "bottom up" and "top down" approaches for protein analysis as well as methods for studying protein conformations are described and illustrated with examples.

1. INTRODUCTION

Structural characterization of proteins is currently delivering new insights into the behavior of individual molecules or large ensembles and recent technological advances have enabled researchers to examine smaller and smaller amounts of biological molecules. Mass spectrometric techniques are capable of analyzing small quantities (down to the level of single molecules)[1] of very large proteins (up to a molecular weight of several megadaltons)[2]. The advent of new ionization techniques such as electrospray ionization (ESI)[3] and matrix-assisted laser desorption/ionization (MALDI)[4] is mainly responsible for these advances. Identification and quantification of proteins from complex mixtures pose

* Corresponding author: Dr. Andrea Sinz, Biotechnological-Biomedical Center, Faculty of Chemistry and Mineralogy, University of Leipzig, Linnéstr.3. D-04103 Leipzig, Germany. Phone: +49-341-9736078. Fax: +49-341-9736115. Email: sinz@chemie.uni-leipzig.de

great challenges for developing novel analytical strategies, as any human cell comprises roughly 10,000 proteins at any particular time, with concentrations that differ at least of a factor of 10[10]. Besides, many proteins are post-translationally modified and are therefore present in several variants. To date, more than 100 modification types are recorded and additional ones are yet to be discovered [5]. Currently, 2D gel electrophoresis (2-DE) in combination with MALDI-TOF mass spectrometry has emerged as the major technology for separation, identification, and quantification of different protein species [6]. However, closer examination of the protein classes, which are routinely identified by 2-DE/MS, suggests that this approach does not represent a truly global technique [7].

A mass spectrometric technique, which has become of increasing importance for protein analysis during the past few years, is Fourier transform ion cyclotron resonance mass spectrometry (FTICRMS)[8; 9]. There are already a number of publications and textbooks giving comprehensive descriptions on mass spectrometry[6;10-12] and especially FTICRMS[13-16] for protein analysis. Therefore, we will just give a short overview on the different aspects of FTICRMS that makes it a valuable tool for analyzing proteins. It is almost certain that the number of applications using this mass spectrometric technique for analyzing complex biological samples will greatly increase in the near future.

2. Basics of FTICR Mass Spectrometry

Among all mass spectrometric techniques, FTICR mass spectrometry offers the highest resolution and mass measurement accuracy [17]. Since its introduction in 1974[8; 9], there have been a number of studies demonstrating these capabilities. For example, Marshall and co-workers resolved more than 11,000 components of crude oil within one broadband mass spectrum [18]. In another experiment, the two peptides RVMRGMR and RSHRGHR whose masses differ by only 0.00045 amu (an electron mass is 0.00055 amu) were baseline resolved [19]. Smith and colleages showed the measurement of 71 peptides from a tryptic digest of bovine serum albumin (BSA) with an average error of 0.77 ppm and a standard deviation of 1 ppm [20]. These impressive data were in most cases acquired on home-built mass spectrometers under conditions, which are not easily reproduced on commercial instruments. However, modern FTICR mass spectrometers offer a resolving power above 100,000 and mass measurement accuracies below 2 ppm on a routine basis. Another point making FTICRMS suitable for analysis of biological samples is that it is a sensitive MS technique. Detection limits for proteins and peptides in low attomole and even zeptomole amounts have been reported [21-24].

The principle underlying FTICR mass spectrometry forms the basis of its unique capabilities. There have been a couple of excellent reviews that give very detailed descriptions about this technique [17;25-27], therefore this article will give only a brief introduction into the basics of FTICRMS. FTMS uses the ICR principle to determine *m/z* values of ions. Ions are trapped in a cell that is located within a static magnetic field (Figure 1). Under the influence of the magnetic field the ions describe a circular motion caused by the Lorentz force and the centrifugal force (inertia) affecting them in opposite directions. Hereby, the angular frequency ω_c of the so-called cyclotron motion depends solely on the *m/z* value of the circulating ions and the magnetic field strength B (Equation 1):

$$\omega_c = B \cdot z/m \quad (1)$$

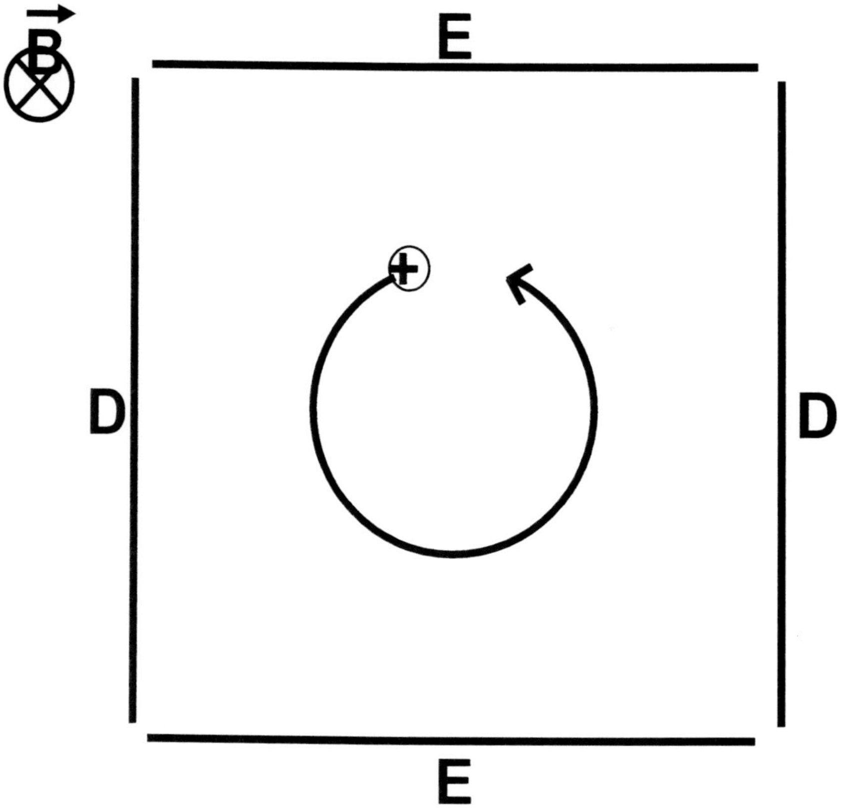

Figure 1. Schematic overview of an ICR cell with excitation (E) and detection electrodes (D).

In order to measure the cyclotron frequency ω_c it is necessary to force the ions of one *m/z* type into coherent motion by applying a frequency pulse through the two opposite excitation electrodes, which is in resonance with the cyclotron frequency of the ions. As an additional result, the kinetic energy of the ions and therefore the radius of the circular motion will increase. After excitation, the circulating ion clouds induce an oscillating image current in the two opposite detection plates whose frequency corresponds to the cyclotron frequency and thus to the *m/z*-values of the ions. A breakthrough in the ICR technique was achieved when Comisarow and Marshall applied inductive detection and Fourier transformation to simultaneously determine the cyclotron frequencies of all ions in the cell after simultaneous excitation by a broadband rf-pulse [8]. The image currents are recorded as a time domain signal, the so-called transient, and after amplification, digitization and Fourier transformation a frequency spectrum is obtained, which is easily converted into a mass spectrum. The high accuracy of this type of mass measurement is primary based on that frequency is not a function of kinetic energy - and hence not influenced by small fluctuations in kinetic energy distribution. Moreover, frequencies can be measured more exactly than any other physical properties.

Another aspect of the ICR technique is that this type of measurement is non-destructive; ions can be stored in the analyzer cell for several minutes or even hours. This offers the opportunity to cool down (either by collisional cooling or by quadrupolar axialization [28;29]) and re-measure the ions in order to increase sensitivity and resolution [30;31]. It is possible to study gas-phase reactions in the cell [32] or to fragment ions by various techniques, e.g., IRMPD [33] (infrared multi-photon dissociation), SORI-CID [34] (sustained off-resonance irradiation collision-induced dissociation), BIRD [35] (blackbody infrared radiative dissociation) or ECD [36] (electron capture dissociation) for MS^n experiments. For this purpose, the ability for selective isolation of ions of one *m/z*-value may also be of great importance. Different isolation techniques have been described, most commonly used are SWIFT [37] (stored-waveform inverse Fourier transformation), CHEF [38] (correlated harmonic excitation waveforms, also as multi-CHEF [39] for selection of multiple ions) and QEA [29;40] (quadrupolar excitation/axialization).

2.1. Tandem Mass Spectrometry

Tandem MS (MS/MS) strategies can be employed to gain structural information about analyte molecules, for example, amino acid sequences can be derived for protein analysis. A comprehensive review about high resolution MS/MS techniques and applications is given by Håkansson *et al.*[41]. Different dissociation techniques are used in connection with FTICRMS in order to fragment isolated ions. Collision-induced dissociation (CID) is performed by pulsing in a neutral gas (Ar, Xe, N_2) before energetic excitation of the ions. Collisions between excited ions and neutral molecules lead to conversion of kinetic energy into internal energy and result in the fragmentation of analyte ions. In the ICR cell, ion activation for CID is mostly achieved by SORI excitation using dipolar radiation with a frequency that is slightly offset from the ions' cyclotron frequency [34]. In comparison to resonant excitation the SORI approach is softer and leads to mass spectra that can be interpreted more easily. Another possibility for energetic fragmentation of ions consists in their irradiation with infrared light. In BIRD this is achieved by thermally heating the environment of the analyzer cell [35]. More frequently used for IR irradiation, however, is the IRMPD approach where activation with a single wavelength infrared laser is used to dissociate the ions [33]. A common feature of all these low-energy dissociation techniques is that they preferably lead to cleavages of the weakest chemical bonds in the molecule. In the case of proteins or peptides, cleavages resulting in the loss of post-translational modifications as well as cleavages of the amide bonds, thus creating b and y type ions [41], occur most frequently. Herein, the relative fragment ion abundances and the fragmentation efficiencies highly depend on the amino acid sequences of the peptides under investigation.

2.2. Electron Capture Dissociation (ECD)

Almost exclusively available for FTICRMS is fragmentation by electron capture dissociation, which was introduced in 1998 by Zubarev *et al.*[36]. This relatively new method offers some unique features for the analysis of peptides and proteins. In contrast to the abovementioned techniques SORI-CID and IRMPD, ECD is believed to proceed by a nonergodic mechanism, which is still under scientific debate. One theory says that the capture of a low-energy electron (<1 eV, applied through a heated filament electron gun [42] or through an indirectly heated dispenser cathode [43] outside the ICR cell) leads to a reduced molecular ion $[M+nH]^{(n-1)+}$, which can release an energetic H•atom [42]. This H•atom can undergo a radical site reaction with a carbonyl group of the peptide, thus initiating backbone cleavage [44]. A modification of this theory was proposed by Leymarie *et al.*[45] based on ECD studies on cyclic peptides. The authors postulate that nonergodic ECD generates an α-carbon radical species that propagates along the protein backbone. This radical migration initiates multiple radical rearrangements, which cause both multiple backbone cleavages and additional side chain cleavages. The preferred formation of c and z· type ions and the more random distribution of cleavage sites agree well with both proposed mechanisms for ECD [46]. The different cleavage sites observed in ECD compared to other MS/MS techniques and its ability to cleave disulfide bonds in proteins [47;48] make ECD a valuable complementary tool for peptide sequencing. A number of studies show exhaustive sequence coverage for peptides and proteins by ECD [44;49].

The use of higher energy electrons (up to 13eV), termed HECD (hot ECD), even allowed distinguishing between the isomeric amino acids Leu and Ile, based on the presence of different d and w type ions after fragmentation of the respective amino acid side chains [50].

Another important characteristic of ECD is that labile bonds of post-translational modifications are not cleaved, thus allowing to map such modifications in peptides and proteins. Various examples demonstrate the analysis of phosphorylated [51;52], glycosylated [53-55], γ-carboxylated and sulphated [56] as well as fatty acid-modified [57] peptides. Acetylation, methylation, and phosphorylation patterns of intact proteins are also amenable to analysis by ECD [58].

One drawback of the ECD technique consists in its low fragmentation efficiency; usually only 5-20% of the precursor ions are cleaved. Especially larger proteins (>20kD) often show a charge reduction, but no fragmentation [42]. The low yield of fragmentation products from large proteins was proposed to have its origin in that ECD cleaves the protein backbone while not disrupting weak non-covalent interactions of the protein's tertiary gas-phase structure [59]. Energetic activation of the cleaved, but still non-covalently attached proteins enables dissociation and detection of the ECD fragments. Therefore, ECD is used in combination with IRMPD or as activated ion (AI) ECD to improve its fragmentation efficiency for proteins [59;60]. On the other hand, the ability of ECD to fragment the protein backbone without cleaving non-covalent interactions is employed for kinetic and structural studies of proteins in the gas-phase [61-64], as will be discussed later.

3. Proteome Analysis

To date, the standard approach for analyzing proteomes is to separate the proteins by 2-DE [65]. After visualization by staining, the protein spots of interest are cut out from the gel, the proteins are enzymatically digested, and the resulting peptide mixtures are analyzed by mass spectrometry to identify the respective protein. Despite its numerous successful applications during the last decade, this 2-DE/MS approach possesses several limitations, which originate mainly from the gel electrophoresis step. 2-DE is a time-consuming technique, which is difficult to reproduce and to automate, and what is even more important:

2-DE cannot handle "extreme" proteins. It is difficult to separate very small, very large, very basic, very acidic, and last but not least, hydrophobic proteins on 2D-gels. To overcome these limitations, efforts have been made to substitute 2-DE by other separation techniques like liquid chromatography or capillary electrophoresis for protein or peptide separation prior to MS analysis [66-73]. In combination with these liquid-based separation techniques, analysis of increasingly complex mixtures is favored over that of a single protein, which greatly enhances sample throughput. FTICRMS has become an efficient tool for proteomics studies, as its superior mass resolution capabilities allow for a simultaneous measurement of numerous compounds, and its high mass measurement accuracy gives additional confidence for subsequent identification of the respective compounds.

Two different strategies are used for protein analysis by FTICR mass spectrometry:

(1) Analysis of proteolytic digests of proteins or protein mixtures ("Bottom-up" approach)
(2) Analysis of intact proteins ("Top-down" approach)

3.1. "Bottom-Up" Analysis

In the "bottom-up" strategy, proteins are specifically cleaved into peptide fragments (mostly by using enzymatic proteolysis) before the peptide mixtures are analyzed by mass spectrometry. To date, the "bottom-up" strategy is the preferred method for protein identification, mainly because peptides are easier to handle compared to large proteins. After 2-DE, which is still the most commonly used technique for protein separation in proteomics, peptides arising from proteolytic cleavage are readily eluted from the gel – a task which is quite difficult to achieve for proteins. Another reason for the attractiveness of the "bottom-up" strategy is that most liquid chromatographic and mass spectrometric techniques are well established for peptides, whereas they are still difficult to realize or less efficient for intact proteins. Identification of proteins is accomplished by two different "bottom-up" strategies. The first one is entitled peptide mass fingerprinting (PMF), in which the parent protein is specifically cleaved to gain a set of peptides that is unique to this protein and as such can be used as a "fingerprint" to identify the original protein by database searching. PMF is broadly applied with conventional MS instrumentation, but only single proteins or simple mixtures can be confidently analyzed. FTICRMS offers some advantages for this type of analysis: With increasing mass measurement accuracy the portion of unique peptide masses for a protein increases significantly [74;75], thus making database searches more confident and allowing protein identifications based on a smaller number of peptides. Together with its high-resolution capabilities, FTICRMS has been shown to be applicable for the analysis of more complex protein mixtures [76]. The analysis of a crude *E. coli* cell extract by LC/FTICRMS has been described recently [77]. Bergquist *et al.* demonstrated the identification of proteins from human body fluids without prior separation or purification. The tryptically digested body fluids were either directly analyzed by ESI-FTICRMS or in combination with LC or capillary electrophoresis to identify proteins in human plasma [78], cerebrospinal fluid [73], urine and saliva [79].

In the second type of "bottom-up" approach, additional information on the protein under investigation is obtained by isolation of selected proteolytic peptides and subsequent fragmentation using MS/MS techniques [80-82]. These tandem MS data offer structural information related to the peptide sequence in addition to information on its mass, thus further increasing the specificity of protein identification. Again, high mass measurement accuracy leads to a more confident data interpretation. A recent publication [83] demonstrates the benefit for *de-novo* sequencing of peptides when additional information from accurate mass determination by FTICRMS is employed. Figure 2 shows the dependence of mass measurement accuracy on the number of possible amino acid compositions (AAC) of peptides, exemplified for the mass 1005.4433 u. With increasing accuracy the calculated set of possible AACs can be significantly reduced and the combination with MS/MS data further limits the number of compositions. Starting with in this way reduced datasets, a relative simple algorithm (composition based sequencing) leads to an unambiguous determination of the respective peptide sequence. As novel FTICR instruments allow accurate mass determinations and online tandem MS experiments at the same time in routine analytical work, the resultant level of more and more exact structural information about the analyzed peptides will make FTICRMS even more valuable for protein analysis.

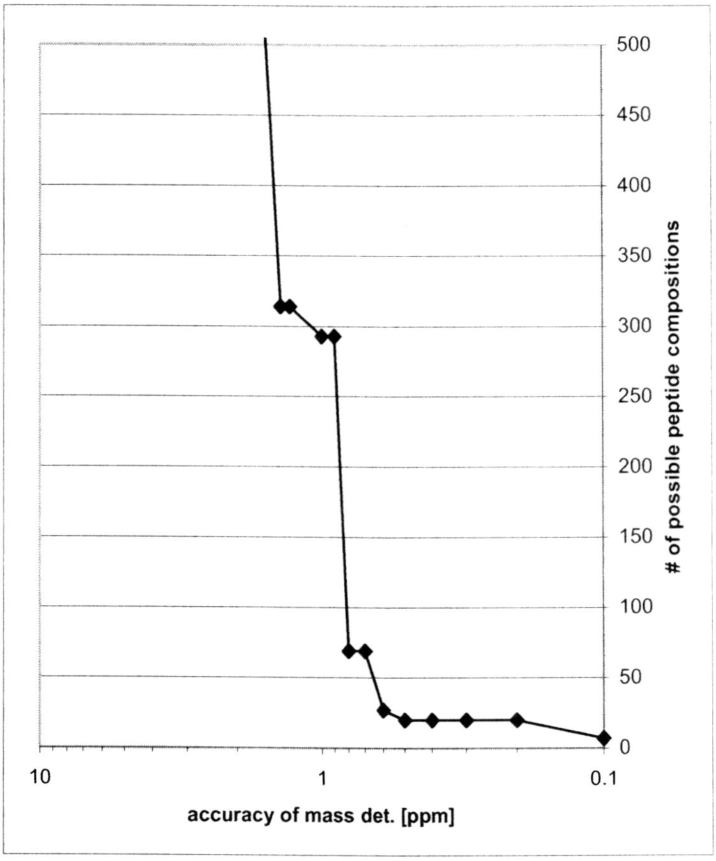

Figure 2: Number of possible amino acid compositions of peptides for a given example mass of 1005.4433 u as depending on the accuracy of mass determination. Calculations were performed including all of the 19 amino acids A C D E F G H (I _ L) K M N P Q R S T V W and Y. Mass calculations correspond to the monomolecular isotopomers of the singly positively charged protonated peptides (C terminus -OH, N terminus -H) (reprinted with permission from reference[83]).

To date, the AMT (accurate mass and time) tag approach, a type of "bottom-up" technique developed by Smith and colleagues [74], has obtained the broadest coverage of one proteome. More than 61% of the predicted proteins of *Deinococcus radiodurans* could be identified with high confidence [84;85] and later improvements even increased the coverage to 83% [85]. For this approach, a library of peptide AMT tags is generated by collecting data from various LC / tandem MS experiments on conventional instruments before peptide masses and LC elution times are validated using LC/FTICRMS. Once a library of AMT tags has been established for an organism, these AMT tags can be used as confident markers for their corresponding proteins in future LC/FTICRMS experiments. This enables high-throughput proteome analysis, given that peptide masses can be determined with sufficient accuracy. As an impressive example, Figure 3 shows the mass versus time plot of ~22,000 detected putative peptides of *D. radiodurans* during a single LC/FTICRMS experiment [75]. About 1,500 AMT tags could be typically matched during one single LC/MS run to about 700 ORFs, corresponding to 15-20% of the predicted proteome of the microorganism.

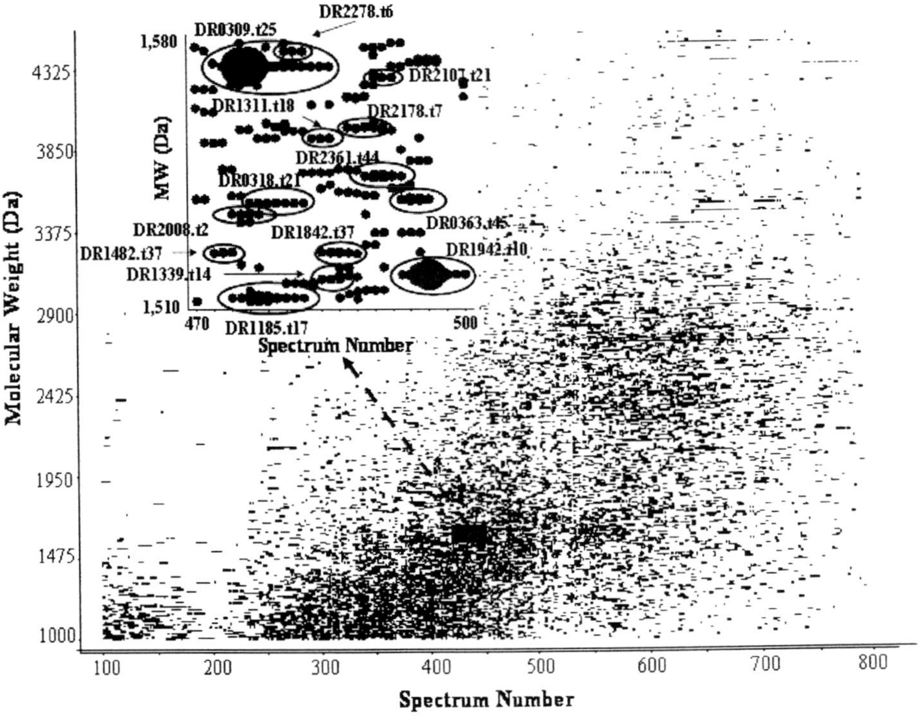

Figure 3: Two-dimensional display of identified AMTs from *Deinococcus radiodurans*. In this display, all of the peptides observed in an LC/FTICR mass spectrometric analysis of the *D. radiodurans* proteome are displayed based on their molecular weight and elution order (i.e., FTICR spectrum number). The circled spots labeled in the inset show spots that were identified as AMTs. The spots are labeled based on their annotation within the organism's genome sequence (i.e., t25: the 25th tryptic peptide counting from the amino terminus, based on complete digestion (reprinted with permission from reference[75]).

3.2. "Top-Down" Analysis

The most direct analytical strategy for protein characterization is based on the analysis of intact proteins instead of proteolytic digests. In this approach, the mass of the intact protein is used together with partial sequence information, derived from tandem MS experiments, for protein identification. Proteins or protein mixtures are usually ionized by electrospray ionization, as this method produces multiply charged ions, which can be measured in a convenient *m/z*-range (< 4000) and are easier to dissociate. After determination of the intact protein's mass, the corresponding protein ions are isolated and dissociated by one of the fragmentation methods available for FTICRMS. Determination of the fragment ion masses and subsequent computing and database matching of parent ion and fragment ion masses lead to protein identification. Even *de-novo* sequencing of proteins is possible if full sequence coverage is obtained after fragmentation, as has been shown for the small protein ubiquitin and the peptide melittin [86]. Because of the high resolution that is required for exact mass measurements of larger proteins and because of its unique abilities to store, isolate, and fragment ions [87], FTICRMS is currently the most widely used MS technique for "top-down" proteomics. A number of studies show the successful application of this approach for protein identifications. Kelleher *et al.* compared different "bottom-up" and "top-down" strategies at the example of carbonic anhydrase. The authors were able to achieve 100% sequence coverage for each top-down approach using SORI-CID on the intact protein or on protein fragments after digestion with BrCN or Lys-C, whereas sequence coverages were 95% and 96% in the "bottom-up" strategie for chymotryptic and Lys-C digestion, respectively[88]. Li *et al.* applied an LC/MS approach for "top-down" analysis of a five protein mixture using IRMPD as fragmentation method. Each of the proteins could be identified out of more than 1000 database candidates [89].

An important advantage of the "top-down" strategy is that detected masses of the intact proteins directly point to modifications, which cannot be predicted from DNA sequence data. Especially in higher organisms, proteins often undergo excessive processing after biosynthesis, including proteolysis and a variety of chemical post-translational modifications (PTMs). In addition, DNA splicing or undiscovered errors in DNA databases lead to differences between the amino acid sequences of expressed proteins and predicted ORFs. The knowledge of the intact protein's mass together with sequence information gained from subsequent MS/MS studies has proved to be a valuable tool for identifying and mapping PTMs or DNA sequence errors. Especially ECD has been shown to be very useful for protein dissociation, as even labile PTMs can be localized [90]. A "top-down" approach has been successfully employed in combination with ECD fragmentation to map different PTMs of histone proteins, such as acetylation, methylation and phosphorylation, which encode for the "histone code" (Figure 4) [58].

4. Analysis of Protein Conformation

Another field of protein analysis deals with the determination of the tertiary structures of proteins. Classical high-resolution methods as NMR and X-ray crystallography are well established and have so far solved a large number of three-dimensional protein structures. In recent years, mass spectrometric methods have matured to become a supplement of these high-resolution techniques, as low-resolution structures of proteins can be determined very fast and with very low sample consumption. Again, the unique features of FTICRMS are of great advantage for studying protein conformations.

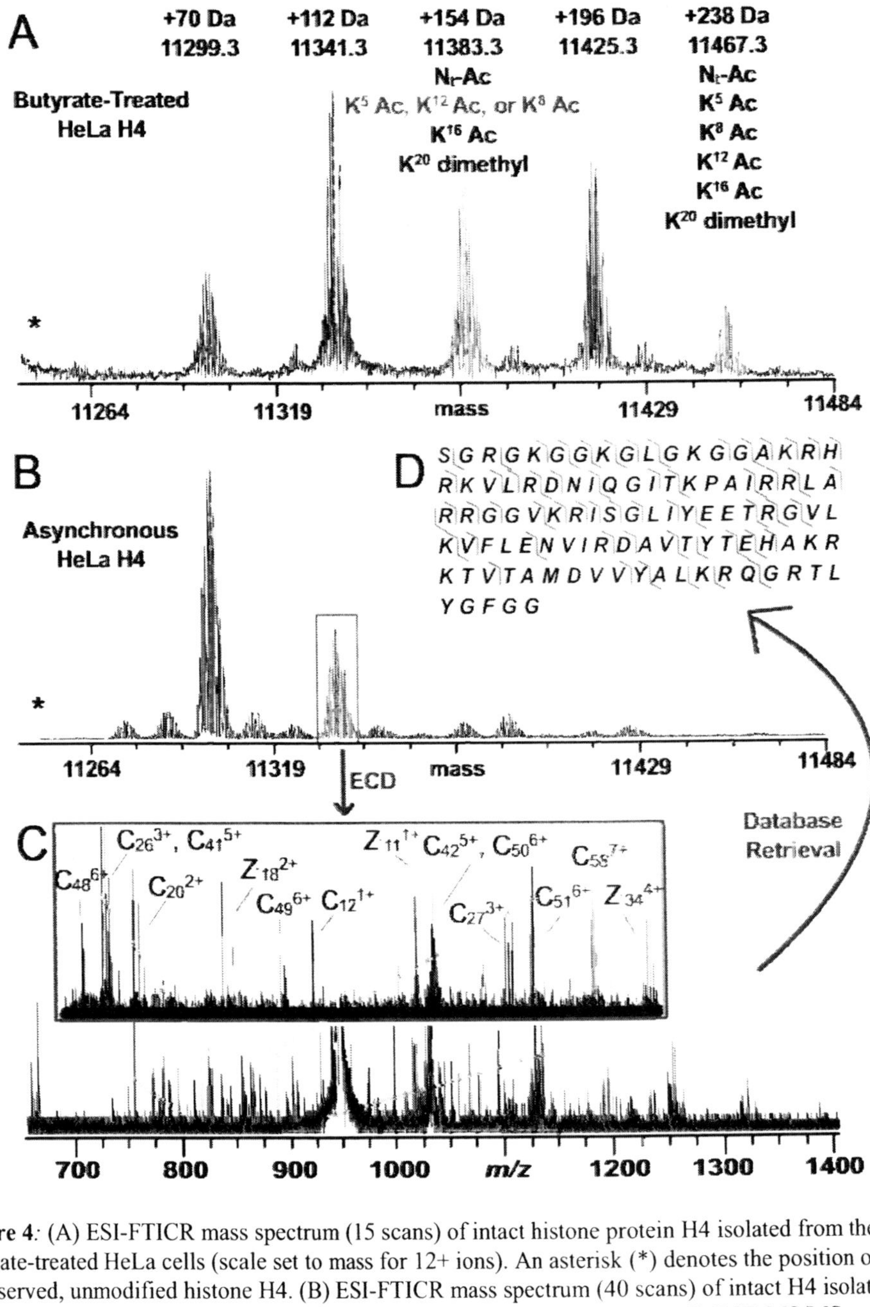

Figure 4: (A) ESI-FTICR mass spectrum (15 scans) of intact histone protein H4 isolated from the butyrate-treated HeLa cells (scale set to mass for 12+ ions). An asterisk (*) denotes the position of the unobserved, unmodified histone H4. (B) ESI-FTICR mass spectrum (40 scans) of intact H4 isolated from the nuclei of asynchronous HeLa cells (scale set to mass for 12+ ions). (C) ECD MS/MS spectrum (107 scans) of a +112 Da modified form of histone H4. (D) ECD fragmentation map of histone H4 +112 Da after streamlined protein characterization achieved by retrieval from a highly annotated database. The best match from the database search is N-terminal acetylation, K16 acetylation, and K20 dimethylation (highlighted in red) (reprinted with permission from reference[58]).

4.1. Chemical Cross-Linking

Chemical cross-linking is a process forming covalent bonds between different molecules (intermolecular) or parts of a molecule (intramolecular) which has proven successful in combination with mass spectrometry as a tool for low-resolution structure determination [91;92]. The goal of performing intramolecular chemical cross-linking of a protein is to get hints on its three-dimensional structure [93], whereas the aim of intermolecular cross-linking between different proteins is to answer, whether or not components interact and how and where they physically contact each other [94;95]. A great variety of cross-linking reagents with different spacer lengths and reactivities can be employed to connect functional groups in proteins (e.g. amine or sulfhydryl groups) and thus measure distances between them. For analyzing cross-linking reaction mixtures FTICRMS represents an attractive tool, as its high mass accuracy serves as an additional constraint in the identification of cross-linking reaction products. Additionally advantageous is that FTICRMS allows a 'gas-phase' purification and subsequent fragmentation of cross-linking products in the ICR cell.

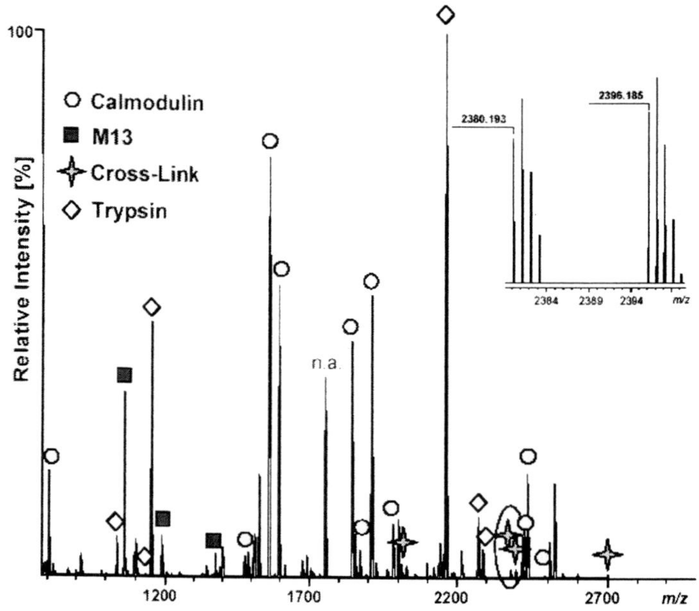

Figure 5: Deconvoluted ESI-FTICR mass spectrum of a tryptic peptide mixture from a complex between calmodulin and the peptide M13, cross-linked with BS^3 (100-fold molar excess over protein/peptide concentration) at an incubation time of 60 min. The insert shows the magnified signal of a cross-linking product at *m/z* 2380.193 between calmodulin residues 75-86 and M13 residues 19-26, which was also detected at *m/z* 2396.185 with one methionine residue oxidized; n.a.: signal not assigned [95].

Both "bottom-up" and "top-down" approaches have been used to analyze cross-linked proteins. The "bottom-up" approach has been applied for mapping protein interfaces, but it has also been successfully employed to determine low-resolution three-dimensional structures of proteins [91]. An ESI-FTICR mass spectrum of a tryptic digestion mixture from a cross-linked complex is presented in Figure 5, which allowed the identification of intermolecular cross-linking products between calmodulin and a peptide derived from skeletal muscle myosin light chain kinase (M13) [95]. The "top-down" approach has so far been demonstrated successful for deducing distance constraints in relatively small proteins, such as ubiquitin [39;96]. The analysis of large protein complexes, however, is likely to be challenging.

4.2. H/D Exchange

H/D exchange employs the relationship between isotopic exchange rates of peptide amide protons in proteins and the protein's secondary and tertiary structure. The theory behind this technique is that the exchange rates of the amide protons are directly related to protein structure characteristics, namely the extent, to which the protons are shielded from the solvent and whether they are involved in intramolecular hydrogen bonding [97-100]. Using ESI and MALDI mass spectrometry, H/D exchange rates are examined by determining the mass increases [101;102]. In order to achieve higher structural specificity, proteins are fragmented after H/D exchange. Again, two strategies are possible; proteins are either proteolytically digested before MS analysis or alternatively, they are physically dissociated inside the MS [103;104]. FTICRMS has been successfully employed for this purpose, e.g., the study of the structural stability of myoglobin has been described by Buijs *et al.*[105]. Another publication deals with the structural investigation of the interface within an enzyme-inhibitor complex [106]. The use of FTICRMS in combination with H/D exchange additionally allows to analyze gas-phase structures, as protein ions can be stored in the analyzer before they are interrogated with gaseous D_2O. Using this method, McLafferty and colleages detected different stable gas-phase conformers of bovine cytochrome *c* [107]. A study of Freitas *et al.* on bradykinins demonstrated the existence of peptide zwitterions in the gas phase [108].

4.3. Fragmentation Studies by ECD

Another possibility to study gas-phase structures of protein ions with FTICRMS consists in performing electron capture experiments. The unique feature of ECD to cleave the amino acid backbone of proteins, whereas non-covalent interactions of tertiary structure are maintained [59] can decrease the efficiency of this technique for protein sequencing, but on the other hand enables the researcher to draw conclusions about gas-phase conformations of proteins. This approach was used for investigation of folding and unfolding characteristics of gaseous ubiquitin depending on charge state and temperature [61;64], as well as for gas-phase folding of cytochrome *c* [63]. A recent publication of Breuker *et al.*[62] described ECD like fragmentation of native cytochrome *c* even without application of external electrons. The fragment ion yield depended on the protein concentration in the ESI solution and could be correlated with cytochrome *c* dimerization. This so-called 'native ECD (NECD)' process was explained by intermolecular electron transfer during protein dimer dissociation. Interestingly, the resulting fragment ions correlated with non-covalent protein-heme interaction in the native structure of cytochrome *c*.

5. Concluding Remarks

In recent years, FTICR mass spectrometry has become an essential tool for analyzing biological macromolecules. In this paper, we described a number of technological and application developments that have strongly contributed for the increasingly important role FTICRMS plays in bioanalytical research. It is likely that the number of applications for solving exciting biological problems using FTICR mass spectrometry will boost in the near future.

Acknowledgements

The junior research group of A.S. is funded by the Saxon State Ministry of Higher Education, Research and Culture. Financial support by the Thermo Electron Corporation (Mattauch-Herzog award of the German Society for Mass Spectrometry to A.S.) is also gratefully acknowledged.

7. References

[1] Twerenbold, D.; Vuilleumier, J.-L.; Gerber, D.; Tadsen, A.; van den Brandt, B.; Gillevet, P. M. *Appl. Phys. Lett.* 1996, *68*, 3503-05.

[2] Heck, A. J. R.; van den Heuvel, R. H. H. *Mass Spectrom. Rev.* 2004, *23*, 368-89.

[3] Fenn, J. B.; Mann, M.; Meng, C. K.; Wong, S. F.; Whitehouse, C. M. *Science* 1989, *46*, 64-71.

[4] Karas, M.; Hillenkamp, F. *Anal. Chem.* 1988, *60*, 2299-301.

[5] Peng, J.; Gygi, S. P. *J. Mass Spectrom.* 2001, *36*, 1083-91.

[6] Mann, M.; Hendrickson, R. C.; Pandey, A. *Annu. Rev. Biochem.* 2001, *70*, 437-73.

[7] Lottspeich, F. *Angew. Chem. Int. Ed.* 1999, *38*, 2476-92.

[8] Comisarow, M. B.; Marshall, A. G. *Chem. Phys. Lett.* 1974, *25*, 282-83.

[9] Comisarow, M. B.; Marshall, A. G. *Chem. Phys. Lett.* 1974, *26*, 489-90.

[10] Yates, J. R., III *Annu. Rev. Biophys. Biomol. Struct.* 2004, *33*, 297-316.

[11] Aebersold, R.; Mann, M. *Nature* 2003, *422*, 198-207.

[12] Gross, J.H., Mass Spectrometry -- A Textbook 2004, Springer, Heidelberg .

[13] Bogdanov, B.; Smith, R. D. *Mass Spectrom. Rev.* 2004, *Published Online*, Mar. 30.

[14] Page, J. S.; Masselon, C. D.; Smith, R. D. *Curr. Opin. Biotech.* 2004, *15*, 3-11.

[15] Bergquist, J. *Curr. Opin. Molec. Ther.* 2003, *5*, 310-14.

[16] Heeren, R. M. A.; Kleinnijenhuis, A. J.; McDonnell, L. A.; Mize, T. H. *Anal. Bioanal. Chem.* 2004, *378*, 1048-58.

[17] Marshall, A. G. *Int. J. Mass Spectrom.* 2000, *200*, 331-56.

[18] Hughey, C. H.; Rodgers, R. P.; Marshall, A. G. *Anal. Chem.* 2002, *74*, 4145-49.

[19] He, F.; Hendrickson, C. L.; Marshall, A. G. *Anal. Chem.* 2001, *73*, 647-50.

[20] Bruce, J. E.; Anderson, G. A.; Wen, J.; Harkewicz, R.; Smith, R. D. *Anal. Chem.* 1999, *71*, 2595-99.

[21] Baykut, G.; Jertz, R.; Witt, M. *Rapid. Commun. Mass Spectrom.* 2000, *14*, 1238-47.

[22] Belov, M. E.; Gorshkov, M. V.; Udseth, H. R.; Anderson, G. A.; Smith, R. D. *Anal. Chem.* 2000, *72*, 2271-79.
[23] Valaskovic, G. A.; Kelleher, N. L.; McLafferty, F. W. *Science* 1996, *273*, 1199-202.
[24] Moyer, S. C.; Budnik, B.; Pittman, J. L.; Costello, C. E.; O'Connor, P. B. *Anal. Chem.* 2003, *75*, 6449-54.
[25] Amster, I. J. *J. Mass Spectrom.* 1996, *31*, 1325-37.
[26] Marshall, A. G.; Hendrickson, C. L.; Jackson, G. S. *Mass Spectrom. Rev.* 1998, *17*, 1-35.
[27] Marshall, A. G.; Hendrickson, C. L. *Int. J. Mass Spectrom.* 2002, *215*, 59-75.
[28] Williams, E. R.; Henry, K. D.; McLafferty, F. W. *J. Am. Chem. Soc.* 1990, *112*, 6157-62.
[29] Speir, J. P.; Gorman, G. S.; Pitsenberger, C. C.; Turner, C. A.; Wang, P. P.; Amster, I. J. *Anal. Chem.* 1993, *65*, 1746-52.
[30] Solouki, T.; Marto, J. A.; White, F. M.; Guan, S.; Marshall, A. G. *Anal. Chem.* 1995, *67*, 4139-44.
[31] Solouki, T.; Paša-Tolic, L.; Jackson, G. S.; Guan, S.; Marshall, A. G. *Anal. Chem.* 1996, *68*, 3718-25.
[32] Nibbering, N. M. M. *Int. J. Mass Spectrom.* 2000, *200*, 27-42.
[33] Little, D. P.; Speir, J. P.; Senko, M. W.; O'Connor, P. B.; McLafferty, F. W. *Anal. Chem.* 1994, *66*, 2809-15.
[34] Gauthier, J. W.; Trautmann, T. R.; Jacobson, D. B. *Anal. Chim. Acta* 1991, *246*, 211-25.
[35] Price, W. D.; Schnier, P. D.; Williams, E. R. *Anal. Chem.* 1996, *68*, 859-66.
[36] Zubarev, R. A.; Kelleher, N. L.; McLafferty, F. W. *J. Am. Chem. Soc.* 1998, *120*, 3265-66.
[37] Marshall, A. G.; Wang, T.-C. L.; Ricca, T. L. *J. Am. Chem. Soc.* 1985, *107*, 7893-97.
[38] de Koning, L. J.; Nibbering, N. M. M.; van Orden, S. L.; Laukin, F. H. *Int. J. Mass Spectrom. Ion. Proc.* 1997, *165*, 209-19.
[39] Kruppa, G. H.; Schnier, P. D.; Tabei, K.; van Orden, S. L.; Siegel, M. M. *Anal. Chem.* 2002, *74*, 3877-86.
[40] Schweikhard, L.; Guan, S.; Marshall, A. G. *Int. J. Mass Spectrom. Ion. Proc.* 1992, *120*, 71-83.
[41] Håkansson, K.; Cooper, H. J.; Hudgins, R. R.; Nilsson, C. L. *Curr. Org. Chem.* 2003, *7*, 1503-25.
[42] Zubarev, R. A.; Horn, D. M.; Fridriksson, E. K.; Kelleher, N. L.; Kruger, N. A.; Lewis, M. E.; Carpenter, B. K.; McLafferty, F. W. *Anal. Chem.* 2000, *72*, 563-73.
[43] Tsybin, Y. O.; Håkansson, P.; Budnik, B. A. *Rapid. Commun. Mass Spectrom.* 2001, *15*, 1849-54.
[44] McLafferty, F. W.; Horn, D. M.; Breuker, K.; Ge, Y.; Lewis, M. E.; Cerda, B. A.; Zubarev, R. A.; Carpenter, B. K. *J. Am. Soc. Mass Spectrom.* 2001, *12*, 245-49.
[45] Leymarie, N.; Costello, C. E.; O'Connor, P. B. *J. Am. Chem. Soc.* 2003, 8958.
[46] Zubarev, R. A.; Haselmann, K. F.; Budnik, B.; Kjeldsen, F.; Jensen, F. *Eur. J. Mass Spectrom.* 2002, *8*, 337-49.
[47] Zubarev, R. A.; Kruger, N. A.; Fridriksson, E. K.; Lewis, M. E.; Horn, D. M.; Carpenter, B. K.; McLafferty, F. W. *J. Am. Chem. Soc.* 1999, *121*, 2857-62.

[48] Kruger, N. A.; Zubarev, R. A.; Carpenter, B. K.; Kelleher, N. L.; Horn, D. M.; McLafferty, F. W. *Int. J. Mass Spectrom.* 1999, *182/183*, 1-5.

[49] Ge, Y.; Lawhorn, B. G.; ELNaggar, M.; Strauss, E.; Park, J.-H.; Begley, T. P.; McLafferty, F. W. *J. Am. Chem. Soc.* 2002, *124*, 672-78.

[50] Kjeldsen, F.; Haselmann, K. F.; Budnik, B. A.; Jensen, F.; Zubarev, R. A. *Chem. Phys. Lett.* 2002, *356*, 201-06.

[51] Stensballe, A.; Jensen, O. N.; Olsen, J. V.; Haselmann, K. F.; Zubarev, R. A. *Rapid. Commun. Mass Spectrom.* 2000, *14*, 1793-800.

[52] Kjeldsen, F.; Haselmann, K. F.; Budnik, B.; Sørensen, E. S.; Zubarev, R. A. *Anal. Chem.* 2003, *75*, 2355-61.

[53] Mormann, M.; Macek, B.; Gonzalez de Peredo, A.; Hofsteenge, J.; Peter-Katalinic, J. *Int. J. Mass Spectrom.* 2004, *234*, 11-21.

[54] Haselmann, K. F.; Budnik, B. A.; Olsen, J. V.; Nielsen, M. L.; Reis, C. A.; Clausen, H.; Johnsen, A. H.; Zubarev, R. A. *Anal. Chem.* 2001, *73*, 2998-3005.

[55] Håkansson, K.; Cooper, H. J.; Emmett, M. R.; Costello, C. E.; Marshall, A. G.; Nilsson, C. L. *Anal. Chem.* 2001, *73*, 4530-36.

[56] Kelleher, N. L.; Zubarev, R. A.; Bush, K.; Furie, B.; Furie, B. C.; McLafferty, F. W.; Walsh, C. T. *Anal. Chem.* 1999, *71*, 4250-53.

[57] Guan, Z. *J. Am. Soc. Mass Spectrom.* 2002, *13*, 1443-47.

[58] Pesavento, J. J.; Kim, Y.-B.; Taylo, G. K.; Kelleher, N. L. *J. Am. Chem. Soc.* 2004, *126*, 3386-87.

[59] Horn, D. M.; McLafferty, F. W. *Anal. Chem.* 2000, *72*, 4778-84.

[60] Tsybin, Y. O.; Ramström, M.; Witt, M.; Baykut, G.; Håkansson, P. *J. Mass Spectrom.* 2004, *39*, 719-29.

[61] Breuker, K.; Oh, H.; Horn, D. M.; Cerda, B. A.; McLafferty, F. W. *J. Am. Chem. Soc.* 2002, *124*, 6407-20.

[62] Breuker, K.; McLafferty, F. W. *Angew. Chem. Int. Ed.* 2003, *42*, 4900-04.

[63] Horn, D. M.; Breuker, K.; Frank, A. J.; McLafferty, F. W. *J. Am. Chem. Soc.* 2001, *123*, 9792-99.

[64] Oh, H.; Breuker, K.; Sze, S. K.; Ge, Y.; Carpenter, B. K.; McLafferty, F. W. *Proc. Natl. Acad. Sci.* 2002, *99*, 15863-68.

[65] Williams, J. D.; Burinsky, D. J. *Int. J. Mass Spectrom.* 2001, *212*, 111-33.

[66] Schrader, W.; Klein, H.-W. *Anal. Bioanal. Chem.* 2004, *379*, 1013-24.

[67] Manabe, T. *J. Chromatogr. B* 2003, *787*, 29-41.

[68] Shen, Y.; Smith, R. D. *Electrophoresis* 2002, *23*, 3106-24.

[69] Shen, Y.; Jacobs, J. M.; Camp II, D. G.; Fang, R.; Moore, R. J.; Xiao, W.; Davis, R. W.; Tompkins, R. G.; Smith, R. D. *Anal. Chem.* 2004, *76*, 1134-44.

[70] Shen, Y.; Tolic, N.; Masselon, C. D.; Paša-Tolic, L.; Camp II, D. G.; Hixson, K. K.; Zhao, R.; Anderson, G. A.; Smith, R. D. *Anal. Chem.* 2004, *76*, 144-54.

[71] Washburn, M. P.; Wolters, D.; Yates, J. R., III *Nature Biotech.* 2001, *19*, 242-47.

[72] Wetterhall M.; Palmblad M.; Håkansson, P.; Markides K.E.; Bergquist J. *J. Proteome* Conrads, T. P.; Anderson, G. A.; Veenstra, T. D.; Paša-Tolic, L.; Smith, R. D. *Anal. Chem.* 2000, *72*, 3349-54.

[73] Smith, R. D.; Anderson, G. A.; Lipton, M. S.; Masselon, C.; Paša-Tolic, L.; Shen, Y.; Udseth, H. R. *OMICS* 2002, *6*, 61-90.

[74] Ihling, C.; Berger, K.; Höfliger, M. M.; Führer, D.; Beck-Sickinger, A. G.; Sinz, A. *Rapid. Commun. Mass Spectrom.* 2003, *17*, 1240-46.
[75] Ihling, C.; Sinz, A. *Proteomics* 2004, *in press.*
[76] Palmblad M.; Wetterhall M.; Markides K.E.; Håkansson, P.; Bergquist, J. *Rapid. Commun. Mass Spectrom.* 2000, *14*, 1029-34.
[77] Bergquist, J.; Palmblad, M.; Wetterhall, M.; Håkansson, P.; Markides, K. E. *Mass Spectrom. Rev.* 2002, *21*, 2-15.
[78] Huang, E. C.; Henion, J. D. *J. Am. Soc. Mass Spectrom.* 1990, *1*, 158-65.
[79] Eng, J. K.; McCormack, A. L.; Yates, J. R., III *J. Am. Soc. Mass Spectrom.* 1994, *5*, 976-89.
[80] McCormack, A. L.; Schieltz, D. M.; Goode, B.; Yang, S.; Barnes, G.; Drubin, D.; Yates, J. R., III *Anal. Chem.* 1997, *69*, 767-76.
[81] Spengler, B. *J. Am. Soc. Mass Spectrom.* 2004, *15*, 703-14.
[82] Lipton, M. S.; Paša-Tolic, L.; Anderson, G. A.; Anderson, D. J.; Auberry, D. L.; Battista, J. R.; Daly, M. J.; Fredrickson, J.; Hixson, K. K.; Konstandarithes, H.; Masselon, C.; Markillie, L. M.; Moore, R. J.; Romine, M. F.; Shen, Y.; Strittmatter, E.; Tolic, N.; Udseth, H. R.; Venkateswaran, A.; Wong, K.-K.; Zhao, R.; Smith, R. D. *Proc. Natl. Acad. Sci.* 2002, *99*, 11049-54.
[83] Paša-Tolic, L.; Lipton, M. S.; Masselon, C.; Anderson, G. A.; Shen, Y.; Tolic, N.; Smith, R. D. *J. Mass Spectrom.* 2002, *37*, 1185-98.
[84] Horn, D. M.; Zubarev, R. A.; McLafferty, F. W. *Proc. Natl. Acad. Sci.* 2000, *97*, 10313-17.
[85] McLafferty, F. W.; Fridriksson, E. K.; Lewis, M. E.; Zubarev, R. A. *Science* 1999, *284*, 1289-90.
[86] Kelleher, N. L.; Lin, H. Y.; Valaskovic, G. A.; Aaserud, D. J.; Fridriksson, E. K.; McLafferty, F. W. *J. Am. Chem. Soc.* 1999, *121*, 806-12.
[87] Li, W.; Hendrickson, C. L.; Emmett, M. R.; Marshall, A. G. *Anal. Chem.* 1999, *71*, 4397-402.
[88] Meng, F.; Forbes, A. J.; Miller, L. M.; Kelleher, N. L. *Mass Spectrom. Rev.* 2004, *published online.*
[89] Sinz, A. *J. Mass Spectrom.* 2003, *38*, 1225-33.
[90] Back, J. W.; de Jong, L.; Muijsers, A. O.; de Koster, C. G. *J. Mol. Biol.* 2003, *331*, 303-13.
[91] Dihazi, G. H.; Sinz, A. *Rapid. Commun. Mass Spectrom.* 2003, *17*, 2005-14.
[92] Schulz, D. M.; Ihling, C.; Clore, G. M.; Sinz, A. *Biochemistry* 2004, *43*, 4703-15.
[93] Kalkhof, S.; Ihling, C.; Mechtler, K.; Sinz, A. *Anal. Chem.* 2004, *Published online*, Dec. 7.
[94] Novak, P.; Young, M. M.; Schoeninger, J.; Kruppa, G. H. *Eur. J. Mass Spectrom.* 2003, *9*, 623-31.
[95] Zhang, Z.; Smith, D. L. *Prot. Sci.* 1993, *2*, 522-31.
[96] Englander, W. S.; Sosnick, T. R.; Englander, J. J.; Mayne, L. *Curr. Opin. Struct. Biol.* 1996, *6*, 18-23.
[97] Kaltashov, I. A.; Eyles, S. J. *Mass Spectrom. Rev.* 2002, *21*, 37-71.
[98] Eyles, S. J.; Kaltashov, I. A. *Methods* 2004, *34*, 88-99.
[99] Katta, V.; Chait, B. T. *J. Am. Chem. Soc.* 1993, *115*, 6317-21.

[100] Thévenon-Emeric, G.; Kozlowski, J.; Zhang, Z.; Smith, D. L. *Anal. Chem.* 1992, *64*, 2456-58.

[101] Palmblad, M.; Buijs, J.; Håkansson, P. *J. Am. Soc. Mass Spectrom.* 2001, *12*, 1153-62.

[102] Kaltashov, I. A.; Eyles, S. J. *J. Mass Spectrom.* 2002, 565.

[103] Buijs, J.; Ramström, M.; Danfelter, M.; Larsericsdotter, H.; Håkansson, P.; Oscarsson, S. *J. Colloid Interface Sci.* 2003, *263*, 441-48.

[104] Akashi, S.; Takio, K. *Prot. Sci.* 2000, *9*, 2497-505.

[105] McLafferty, F. W.; Guan, Z.; Haupts, U.; Wood, T. D.; Kelleher, N. L. *J. Am. Chem. Soc.* 1998, *120*, 4732-40.

[106] Freitas, M. A.; Marshall, A. G. *Int. J. Mass Spectrom.* 1999, *182/183*, 221-31.

PAPERS

In: Principles of Biomacromolecular Mass Spectrometry ISBN 1-60021-063-5
Editor: Simone Koenig, pp. 57-73

Chapter 3

IDENTIFICATION OF TYROSINE-O-SULFATION AS POST-TRANSLATIONAL MODIFICATION OF MELANOMA INHIBITORY ACTIVITY (MIA) PROTEIN

Marcel P. de Vries, Nicole C.C.J.M. Rullens-Ligtvoet, Wouter J. Hoeberichts, Alain J. van Gool, Mario J.M. van Zeeland, Milou Kouwijzer, Gijs F. Verheijden, Annemieke M.H. Boots, Peter D.E.M. Verhaert*, and Ebo S. Bos[♦]

Departments of Target Discovery and Pharmacology, NV Organon, PO Box 20, 5340 BH Oss, the Netherlands

*Flemish Interuniversity Institute for Biotechnology; Laboratoire pour Spectrometrie de Masse, Institut de Chimie B6c, Université de Liège, B-4000 Liège; Biomedical Research Institute, Limburgs Universitair Centrum, B-3590 Diepenbeek; and Laboratory for Neuroplasticity and Neuroproteomics, Naamsestraat 59, B-3000 Leuven, Belgium

ABSTRACT

Matrix assisted laser desorption ionization time-of-flight mass spectrometry (MALDI-TOF MS) and isoelectric focusing (IEF) of pure recombinant human MIA (melanoma inhibitory activity) protein, as expressed in CHO cells, indicated that part of the protein was post-translationally modified.

Whereas standard positive ion mode MALDI analysis of intact MIA revealed an additional peak 80 Da higher than the theoretical mass, IEF showed three major protein bands which could all unequivocally be identified as MIA isoforms by peptide mass fingerprinting.

Negative ionization MALDI mass spectrometry on a quadrupole TOF instrument indicated that the differences between these isoforms were due to one or two 80 Da modifications confined to tryptic fragment 59-76. The identity of the 80 Da post-translational modification

[♦] Corresponding author: Dr. Ebo Sijbren Bos, NV Organon, Molenstraat 110, PO Box 20, 5340 BH Oss, the Netherlands. Tel: +31 412 662668. Fax: +31 412 662542 E-mail: ebo.bos@organon.com

(PTM) was determined to be a Tyr-O-sulfation through enzymatic removal of the 80 Da moiety from MIA by arylsulfatase treatment, and through the absence of the 80 Da modification(s) in MIA harvested from cells cultured in the presence of chlorate, which is known to inhibit Tyr-O-sulfation. The PTM being sulfation was further corroborated by its metastability upon MALDI-TOF MS analysis. It is concluded that the CHO produced MIA is partially post-translationally modified by Tyr-O-sulfation at positions 69 and/or 70 (^{59}LFWGGSVQGD**YY**GDLAAR^{76}).

Protein Tyr-O-sulfation, has been reported to serve various functions, including modulation of protein-protein interactions. Combination of this notion with the observation that the eukaryotic MIA protein shows only a weak binding towards laminin and fibronectin leads to the speculation that the putative *in vivo* metastasis promoting activity of MIA may be based on the interaction of MIA with an as yet unknown factor via Tyr-(O)-sulfation enhanced binding kinetics.

INTRODUCTION

Melanoma inhibitory activity (MIA) or cartilage-derived retinoic acid-sensitive protein (CD-RAP) is an 11 kDa secretory protein which is normally expressed by cartilage, but is also produced by malignant melanomas and chondrosarcomas and to a lesser extent by adenocarcinomas including breast and colon cancers [1]. Human MIA/CD-RAP (huMIA) is translated as a 131 amino acid precursor and is processed into a mature, non-glycosylated 107 aa protein by cleavage of a secretion signal peptide. The tertiary structure of *E. coli* produced rec huMIA revealed an SH3-resembling molecule stabilized by two disulfide bridges [2-4], yielding a final protein product with a calculated molecular mass of 12106 Da.

Originally, Blesch *et al.* identified MIA as a factor secreted by melanoma cells that was able to inhibit their growth *in vitro* [5]. However, further studies revealed expression patterns inconsistent with tumor suppression and indicated that MIA may actually promote melanoma metastasis *in vivo* [6]. Expression of the MIA gene was not detected in normal skin, but was associated with progression of melanocytic tumors [6]. Also, increased expression of MIA in melanoma cells was reported to enhance their metastatic potential when injected into hamsters [7].

MIA shares structural homology with the binding pockets of α4β1 and α5β1 integrins as was concluded from the finding that antibodies inhibiting binding of integrin to fibronectin cross-react with MIA [8]. The distal loop comprising residues Asp 68 to Ala 75 of MIA resembles a sequence in laminin that has been implicated in recognition of α2β1 integrin [3]. Furthermore, it is suggested by Bosserhoff *et al.* [9], that the MIA protein specifically inhibits attachment of melanoma cells to fibronectin and laminin by masking the binding sites of integrins to these extracellular matrix proteins, thus promoting invasion and metastasis *in vivo*.

In normal tissues, MIA is expressed primarily by chondrocytes. Its expression begins at chondrogenesis and continues through development and in mature chondrocytes, indicating that MIA is fundamental to the cartilage cell phenotype [10]. The level of MIA/CD-RAP in synovial fluid reflects remodeling of articular cartilage and may be used as a marker for restorative reaction of chondrocytes [11].

Most of the recent studies on MIA structure and metastasis-promoting activity have been performed with recombinant MIA protein produced by *E. coli* [2,3,12]. In order to obtain human MIA that is produced under mammalian expression conditions, thus avoiding the possibly troublesome process of protein denaturation and refolding from inclusion bodies we opted for overexpression of MIA by stable transfection into Chinese hamster ovary (CHO) cells.

Recombinant huMIA purified from conditioned medium of CHO-transfectants showed an extra +80 Da peak upon matrix assisted laser desorption ionization time-of-flight mass spectrometry (MALDI-TOF MS) analysis, as well as multiple bands in isoelectric focusing (IEF). In this report, we characterize these MIA protein forms as specific post-translational modifications (Tyr-O-sulfation). The possible implications of this finding for the putative role of MIA in metastasis formation are discussed.

MATERIAL AND METHODS

Expression and Purification of huMIA

Human MIA (huMIA) cDNA was isolated by PCR and subsequently stably transfected into CHO-K1 cells using the expression vector pNGV-1 to yield transfectants that secreted MIA under serum-free culture conditions. From the pool of transfectants a producer cell line was selected with expression levels of approximately 50 mg/L.

MIA was purified to near homogeneity from culture supernatants by capture on a cation exchange column SP-Sepharose equilibrated in 0.2 mol/L NaCl; 0.02 mol/L sodium phosphate pH 7.4. MIA was eluted with 0.5 mol/L NaCl; 0.02 mol/L sodium phosphate pH 7.4, concentrated and subjected to size exclusion chromatography on a Superdex-75 column equilibrated in 0.5 mol/L NaCl; 0.02 mol/L sodium phosphate pH 7.4 Fractions containing pure MIA as determined by SDS-PAGE were pooled, concentrated to around 2 g/L and stored at -20°C.

SDS- Page

SDS-PAGE was carried out in 4-12% NuPAGE gels (Invitrogen, Breda, the Netherlands) using MOPS as running buffer essentially according to the manufacturer's instructions. After fixation for 30 min in 200 g/L TCA, gels were stained with colloidal Coomassie Brilliant Blue [13].

Determination of Melanoma Inhibitory Activity

Melanoma inhibitory activity of the eukaryotic huMIA was determined on G-361/CRL 1424, HT-144, SK-MEL-1, SK-MEL-3/HTB 69 1, SK-MEL-24 and SK-MEL-31 cells essentially as described [14]. In part of the experiments, MIA had been extensively dialyzed against 0.1 mol/L acetic acid for at least 16h prior to incubation with the melanoma cells [14].

Biomolecular Interaction Analysis (BIA)

All BIA experiments were carried out on a Biacore 3000 analyzer.

For quantitative binding studies of MIA to ECM proteins laminin and fibronectin the following experiment was performed.

Human placental laminin and human plasma fibronectin (both from Sigma, Zwijndrecht, the Netherlands) were immobilized by amine coupling on a CM5 chip. The immobilization levels were 8240 response units (RU) and 9534 RU, respectively. Bovine serum albumin (BSA), immobilized to a level of 11482 RU, was used as a control, which enables proper comparison with previously published results [2]. Subsequently, 50 μL of a dilution series of rec huMIA in HBS-EP buffer (Biacore, Breda, the Netherlands, consisting of 0.01 mol/L Hepes, 0.15 mol/L NaCl, 3 mmol/L EDTA, 50 mg/L P20) with concentrations ranging between 6.25 and 50 mg/L were injected at a flow rate of 10 μL/min, followed by 70 μL of HBS-EP buffer (all at 25°C). Finally, the surface was regenerated with a 30 s injection of 10 mmol/L HCl. Combination plots and K_{aff} calculations were made using BIAevaluation software (Biacore) with the BSA signal subtracted [15]. At the level of MIA binding observed mass transport limitation is not considered an issue.

In order to investigate whether the PTM of MIA was tyrosine-O-phosphorylation, the following experiment was carried out.

Mab 4G10, an anti-phosphotyrosine IgG2b/κ (Upstate, Dundee, UK), and the isotype control were immobilized on a CM5 chip by amine coupling to levels of 5980 and 5664 RU respectively. Twenty-five μL of 25 mg/L rec MIA in HBS-EP buffer was injected at a flow rate of 5 μL/min followed by 70 μL of HBS-EP buffer. A solution of 25 mg/L of a Tyr-O-phosphorylated peptide (viz. biotinylated ITAM1 peptide: KRSGLY(P)NELNKGR-REEY(P)DVLD, Mw 2941 Da) was used as a positive control. Regeneration was achieved through a 30 s injection of 10 mmol/L HCl. Combination plots were made using BIAevaluation software (Biacore) with the isotype control signal subtracted [15].

Isoelectric Focusing (IEF)

IEF gels (5%T, 3% C, 125×240×0.5 mm), were cast using 40 g/L Servalyt 3-10 IsoDalt (Serva, Heidelberg, Germany) as ampholytes. The gel contained 4 mol/L urea in order to circumvent solubility problems of MIA at low ionic strength. A 30 min pre-run was carried out at 2000V, 10 mA and 10 W. Subsequently, 25 μg of lyophilized MIA (extensively dialyzed against 0.3 mol/L NH_4Ac) were dissolved in 4 mol/L urea and applied on the gel. Focusing was carried out for 3 h at 2000 V, 10 mA and 10 W and for 30 min at 2000V, 20 mA and 20 W. Gels were stained with colloidal Coomassie Brilliant Blue [13] after fixation in 200 g/L TCA (30 min). The various bands representing MIA isoforms were quantified using a GS-700 imaging densitometer (Bio-Rad Laboratories, Hercules CA, USA).

Identification of IEF Bands with Mass Spectrometry

Coomassie-stained bands, representing MIA isoforms were excised from the IEF gel and processed for Peptide Mass Fingerprinting (PMF). The gel plugs were washed [2x in H_2O], shrunk [2x in acetonitrile] and dried (*in vacuo* centrifugation in a SpeedVac system). In gel protein digestion was allowed to take place overnight (37°C) in a minimal volume (15-30 μL) of 25 mmol/L NH_4CO_3 (pH 8.0) containing 12.5 mg/L porcine trypsin (Promega, Leiden, The Netherlands). The resulting samples were acidified by addition of 1 μL HCOOH prior to concentration and desalting on self-made reversed phase microcolumns [GELoader tip (Eppendorf, Hamburg, Germany) fitted with 0.3-0.5 μL POROS20R2 (Applied Biosystems, Framingham, MA, USA)]. PMF spectra were recorded by MALDI-TOF MS on a Voyager DE Pro (Applied Biosystems, Framingham, MA, USA). The system was used in reflectron mode, with delayed extraction. Alpha-cyano-4-hydroxycinnamic acid (αCHCA) was employed as matrix (2.5 g/L in 300 mL/L acetonitrile; 1mL/L TFA). Mass spectra were externally calibrated using two tryptic BSA fragments (m/z 927.49 and 2045.03). The samples were measured both in positive and negative ionization mode. The spectra were processed using Data Explorer processing software (Applied Biosystems, Framingham, MA, USA).

MALDI-TOF MS Analysis of Intact MIA

MALDI-TOF spectra of the intact (undigested) protein were obtained in sinapinnic acid (SA) with the Voyager DE Pro in linear delayed extraction mode, using a two point external calibration (on myoglobin at m/z 16953 $[MH^+]$ and 8477 $[MH2^+/2]$). Prior to analysis, the samples were desalted and concentrated on μC18-ZipTips (Millipore Corporation, Billerica MA, USA). Elution was directly onto a stainless steel MALDI target in 1 μL of a solution containing 10 g/L SA in 500 mL/L ACN/ 1 mL/L TFA.

MS/MS Analysis of MIA Tryptic Digests

Purified, lyophilized huMIA was taken up in 25 mmol/L NH_4HCO_3 (pH 8.0) containing 12.5 mg/L porcine trypsin (Promega, Leiden, the Netherlands) and digested in solution. MS and MS/MS spectra were recorded on an orthogonal MALDI quadrupole TOF hybrid instrument (QSTAR-Pulsar*i*, Applied Biosystems, Framingham, MA, USA). Of the digest 0.5 μL was directly spotted onto a stainless steel target and 0.5 μL of a highly concentrated matrix solution (160 g/L 2,5 dihydroxybenzoic acid (DHB) in 330 mL/L ACN / 1mL/L TFA) were added. MS spectra were recorded and peptide masses were selected for CID (collision induced dissociation) tandem MS fragmentation analysis. Argon was used as collision gas and collision energies were adjusted for each precursor ion by real time monitoring of the fragment spectrum. The identified peptide sequences were interpreted considering a theoretically calculated digest of MIA (SwissProt accession # Q16674).

Nuclear Magnetic Resonance (NMR)

A ^{31}P-1D experiment to detect ^{31}P-nuclei present in the sample was performed on MIA (7 g/L in 0.5 mol/L NaCl; 20 mmol/L phosphate buffer pH 7.0). The measurement was performed on a 400 MHz Bruker DPX spectrometer and recorded using the os_p31cpd parameter set in a proton-decoupled fashion (8192 spectra).

Sulfatase Treatment of MIA

Fifteen U of aryl-sulfatase type VIII (Sigma, Zwijndrecht, the Netherlands) were added to 32 µg of recMIA in 1 mol/L NH_4Ac buffer (pH 6.0) and the reaction mixture was incubated for 3 h at 37°C. MALDI-TOF spectra of enzyme-treated and control MIA preparations were obtained in SA as described above.

Part of the samples were dialyzed against 0.3 mol/L NH_4Ac, lyophilized overnight and dissolved in 4mol/L urea for IEF analysis as described above.

MIA Expression in the Presence of Chlorate

MIA-expressing CHO transfectants were cultured till confluence in DMEM/F12 containing 50ml/L Fortified, 62.5 mg/L penicillin and 62.5 mg/L streptomycin, corresponding with approximately 10^8 cells per 490 cm^2 roller bottle. The adhering cells were washed with fresh medium and the cell culture was continued in similar medium in the presence and absence of 20 mmol/L $NaClO_3$. After 48h, supernatants were harvested, MIA was purified according to standard procedures and analyzed by IEF and MALDI-TOF MS as described above.

RESULTS

Purification and Functional Analysis of Rec huMIA

Rec huMIA was purified from cell culture medium by cation exchange chromatography on SP-Sepharose FF and size exclusion chromatography on Superdex 75 as described under Materials and Methods. This yielded virtually pure MIA as judged by SDS-PAGE (Fig.1). Based on ELISA measurements, the average total recovery in 5 experiments was around 70%. The molecular mass of the intact protein of 12106 as measured by MALDI-TOF MS, the peptide mass fingerprint and MS/MS analysis of the tryptic peptides identified the isolated protein as human MIA. It was recognized by and could be quantified with the commercially available MIA ELISA (Roche Applied Science, Mannheim, Germany).

As part of the quality control, the final product was assessed for melanoma inhibitory activity on a series of cell lines as outlined in the Materials and Methods section. In contrast to our expectations, none of the MIA batches prepared showed growth-inhibiting activity (data not shown), not even after prolonged acid treatment which is claimed to enhance the *in vitro* activity considerably [14].

As was published by several authors, *E.coli*-produced MIA exhibits high affinity binding to laminin and fibronectin [1-3]. Binding studies of our CHO-produced rec huMIA to these ECM proteins were performed through BIA using laminin and fibronectin as immobilized ligands and MIA as analyte in solution. From the results presented in Fig. 2, it is concluded that both the MIA-laminin and MIA-fibronectin interactions are characterized by fast on/fast off kinetics at binding affinities of 15 µmol/L and 5 µmol/L respectively.

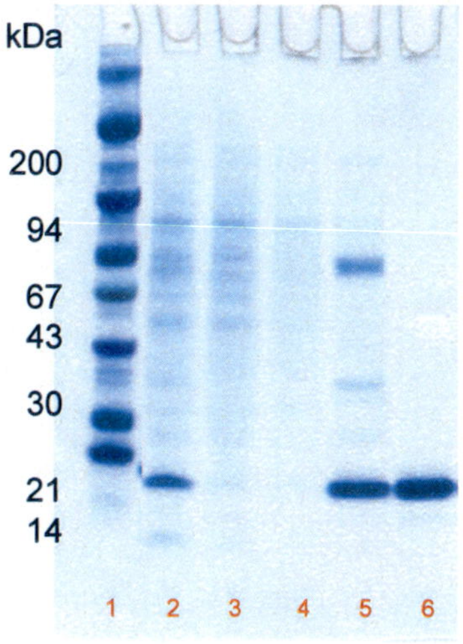

Figure 1. SDS PAGE analysis of huMIA purification
Lane 1, prestained MW markers (Amersham Biosciences); lane 2, conditioned medium of CHO transfectant; lane 3, fall-through of SP column; lane 4, wash SP column; lane 5, eluate SP column; lane 6, huMIA after SEC on Superdex-75.

MALDI-TOF MS Indications for a Post-Translational Modification of huMIA

(1) MALDI-TOF analysis of the purified protein (Fig. 3A) revealed the expected peak at m/z 12105 for mature MIA. However, an additional peak at m/z 12185 was observed corresponding to the theoretical molecular weight plus 80 Da. The size difference between the two peaks suggested a post-translational modification either by (Tyr) sulfation (80.0642 Da) or phosphorylation (79.9799 Da).

(2) Following reduction, alkylation and in-solution trypsin digestion of the MIA preparation, the 80 Da modification was not observed in positive ion mode reflectron MALDI-PMF analysis. However, switching the ionization polarity in the source of the MS instrument (negative ion mode MALDI-TOF PMF), did allow for a +80 Da peak to be detected associated with tryptic peptide ^{59}LFWGGSVQGDYYGDLAAR^{76}: next to the expected signal for the deprotonated tryptic peptide (AA 59-76) at m/z 1972, an additional signal of m/z 2052 was observed (Fig. 3B). The sequence of this peptide contains two adjacent tyrosine residues (Tyr^{69} and Tyr^{70}), which could be substrates for either phosphorylation or sulfation.

(3) IEF analysis of rec huMIA revealed the presence of three major isoforms (I, IIa and III, as indicated in Fig. 4). The apparent pI of the most basic isoform corresponds with unmodified MIA (predicted pI 9.6). Using densitometry scanning, the relative intensities of these bands were determined to be 78%, 18%, and 5% respectively. Bands were excised from the IEF gel, reduced, alkylated and in-gel digested by trypsin after which the digest was subjected to MS analysis (Fig. 5).

As before, only negative ion mode MALDI-PMF allowed detection of the +80 Da modification in IEF bands IIa and III (Fig. 5). The spectrum of band I, the most basic isoform, showed a major peak at m/z 1972 corresponding with the deprotonated tryptic peptide ($[M\text{-}H]^-$) ^{59}LFWGGSVQGDYYGDLAAR^{76}, a non-modified fragment of MIA protein. Bands IIa and III yielded an additional peak at m/z 2052. This corresponds with the mass of fragment 59-76 increased by +80 Da (Fig. 5).

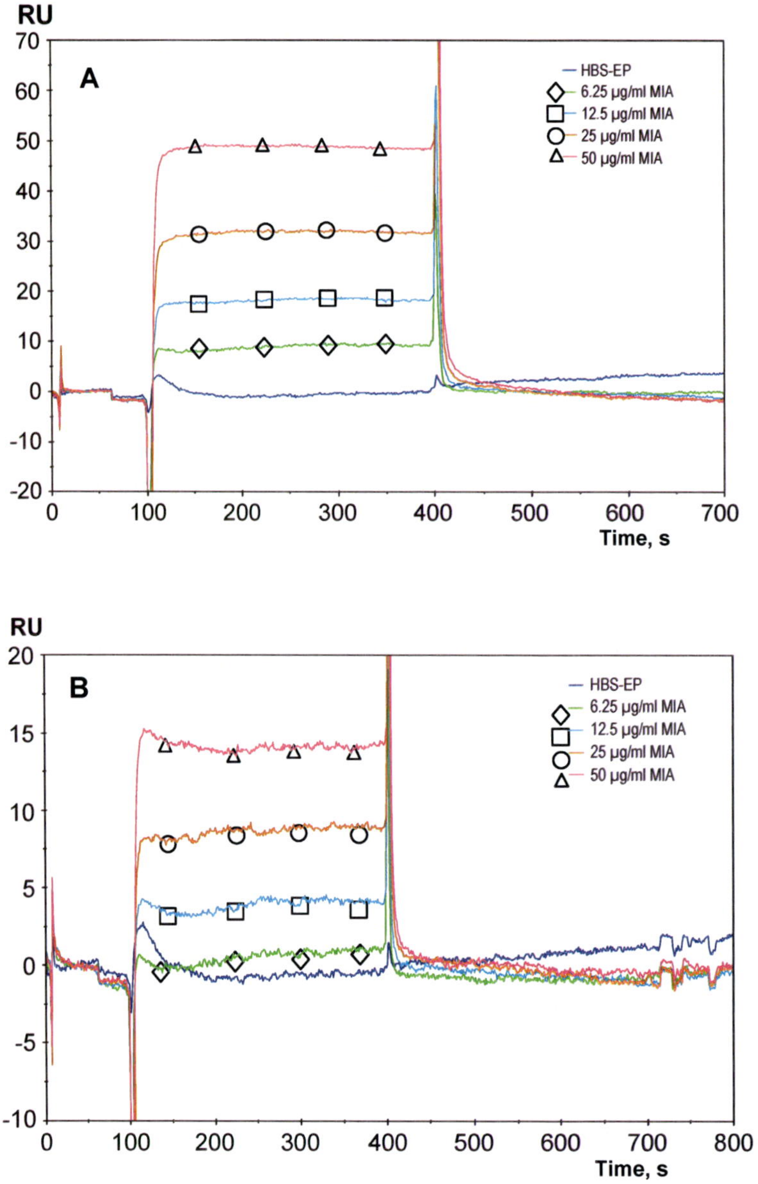

Figure 2. BIA of huMIA binding to ECM proteins laminin (A) and fibronectin (B)
Both proteins were immobilized to the chip, whereas huMIA was employed as soluble analyte. K_{aff} values were calculated according to a 1:1 Langmuir binding model (employing BIAevaluation software) and were 15µmol/L for the MIA-laminin interaction and 5 µmol/L for the MIA-fibronectin interaction, respectively.

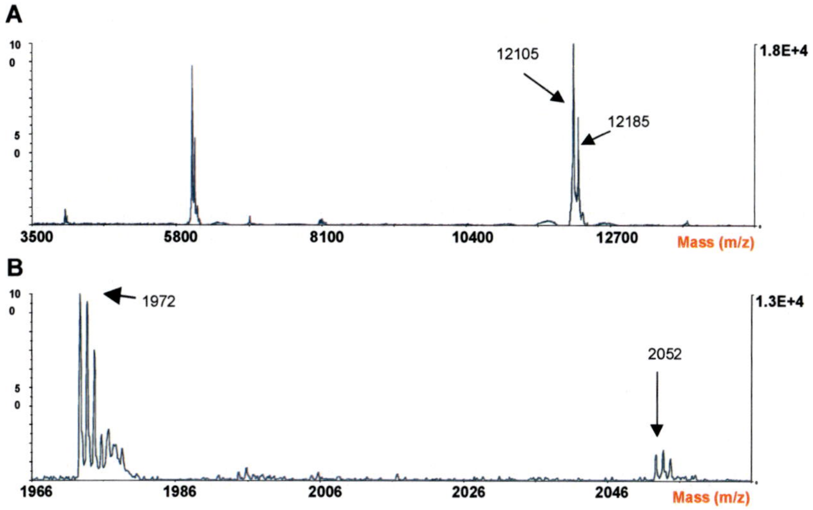

Figure 3. MALDI-TOF analysis of huMIA

A. Intact huMIA analysis. Arrows point to the 12105 Da peak representing unmodified MIA and the 12185 Da peak, representing MIA containing a +80 Da PTM. The peaks at m/z 6052 and 6092 represent the doubly charged ions [M+2H/2]+.

B. Negative-ion MALDI-TOF MS PMF analysis (detail). Both MIA tryptic peptide 59-76 (m/z 1972) and its +80 Da modified variant (m/z 2052) are indicated. (The poorly resolved ion cluster following the well resolved 1972 isotope pattern is indicative of metastability of a fraction of higher mass peptide ions present in the preparation, see text and Fig. 4).

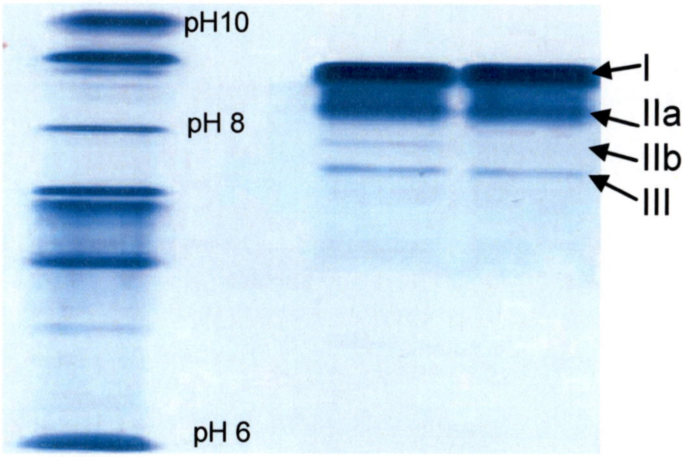

Figure 4. Isoelectric focussing of purified rec huMIA

Lane 1, Serva 3-10 IEF marker; lane 2 and 3, two different MIA preparations. The three major bands representing different isoforms of huMIA are indicated.

(4) A detailed comparative analysis of selected peaks observed in the MALDI-TOF spectra of separately excised bands I to III (Figs. 4-6) is quite revealing for ascribing the +80 Da PTM to either phosphorylation or sulfation.

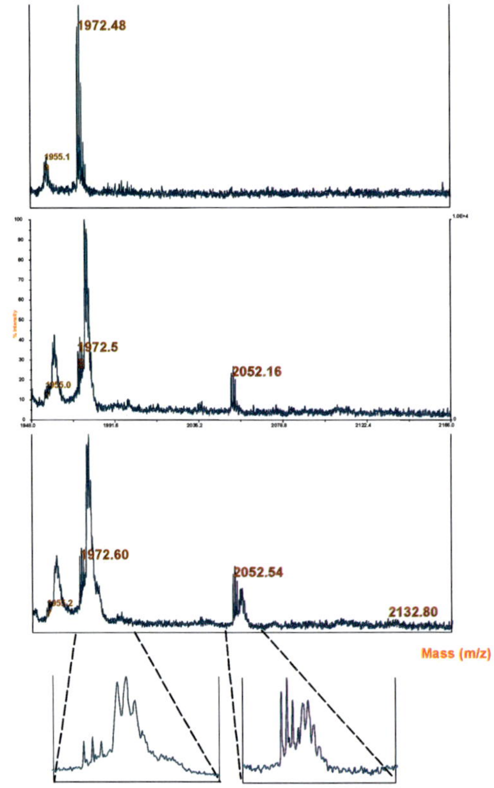

Figure 5. MALDI-TOF MS negative ionisation mode PMF analysis of huMIA IEF bands I, II & III (upper, middle and lower trace respectively; selected mass range)
Details from lower panel show resolved isotopic clusters of MIA tryptic fragment 59-76 with and without a +80 Da modification (right and left panel respectively), with the superimposed metastable ion cluster from the PSD fragmentation of the same tryptic peptide with one and two +80 Da modifications.

(4a) Phosphorylated ions are reported to be relatively stable in MALD-TOF MS. Next to some other characteristic fragments, Ser-, Thr- and Tyr-phosphorylated peptide ions can generally be readily detected as +80 Da peaks in positive ion mode [16]. This, however, does not appear the case for the +80 Da peptide ions observed here.

(4b) Peptide ions containing Tyr-sulfate side chains are described to be considerably more labile as compared to Tyr-phosphorylated ones, which is reflected in their metastable fragmentation behavior [17]. Tyr-sulfated peptide ions readily lose their sulfate moiety (-80 Da) in the mass spectrometer flight tube. As this decay occurs ‘post source’ somewhere during the ion drift along the flight tube of the MALDI-TOF instrument, the fragment ions will not be focused onto a reflectron detector. This results in an isotopic cluster less resolved than that of in-source generated ions [18]. Therefore, post-source decay (PSD) ions have a higher apparent m/z than the in-source fragmented ions as the former have been traveling undegraded for part of the time-of-flight tube. In a conventional MALDI-TOF instrument, peptide ions losing their sulfate moiety within the MS source are mass spectrometrically indistinguishable from non-sulfated peptide ions, with the typical well resolved isotopic pattern. This observation has formerly been used to discriminate between sulfotyrosine and phosphotyrosine in both electrospray [19] and MALDI [20], and for more general detection of PTMs in positive ion mode reflectron MALDI-TOF MS [21].

Our results show band I with a well resolved isotope pattern at m/z 1972, corresponding with $[M-H]^-$ (deprotonated peptide ion) of the unmodified tryptic fragment 59-76 (Fig. 5, upper panel). Band IIa exhibits an additional, well resolved peak at 2052, representing the +80 Da modification of the same fragment (Fig. 5 middle panel). In the same spectrum of band IIa, the resolved isotopes at m/z 1972 are overshadowed by a peak cluster of noticeably reduced resolution with an apparent m/z value of 1976 (Fig. 5 lower two panels). These appear as metastable (PSD) ions according to Harvey *et al.* [18]. The data are fully consistent with a Tyr-O-sulfation on the 59-76 fragment, with the resolved signal at m/z 2052 representing a small fraction of the ions reaching the detector intact.

Likewise, MALDI-PMF of band III showed metastable ions at m/z 1976 and 2056, and well resolved signals at m/z 1972 and m/z 2052 respectively (Fig. 5). This would indicate the presence of a second sulfate group on the already sulfated 2052 peptide. As indicated above, two sulfations can indeed occur on two adjacent tyrosine residues in this peptide (^{59}LFWGGSVQGD**YY**GDLAAR^{76}). A similar observation of double sulfation has been reported before for recombinant factor VIII [22] and glycoprotein 1b-α [23]. In the linear MALDI-TOF MS mode (which does not allow the detection of post-source decay fragments), well resolved peaks at m/z 1972, 2052 as well as at m/z 2132 are detectable in band III, supporting the hypothesis of these ions being the result of metastable decay (data not shown).

(4c) In this respect, also the MS analyses in the orthogonal MALDI quadrupole-TOF hybrid instrument are quite enlightening. In this MS instrument, source and analyzer are fully decoupled, with the ions leaving the source efficiently cooled, so that PSD metastability is not likely to be as prominent as in conventional MALDI-TOF systems. Ions which do fragment in the quadrupole section of the instrument prior to entering the TOF analyzer are all focused on the MS detector (see Fig. 6). Negative-ionization MALDI-Q-TOF-MS of band IIa and III (the more acidic isoforms), reveals much less fragmentation than in the MALDI-TOF analyses (Fig. 6). A substantially larger proportion of the ions reach the detector unfragmented. Hence, more pronounced peaks at 2052 in band IIa and III, and even a additional peak at m/z 2132, which corresponds with the mass of AA59-76 MIA peptide with two +80 Da additions are detected (Fig. 7).

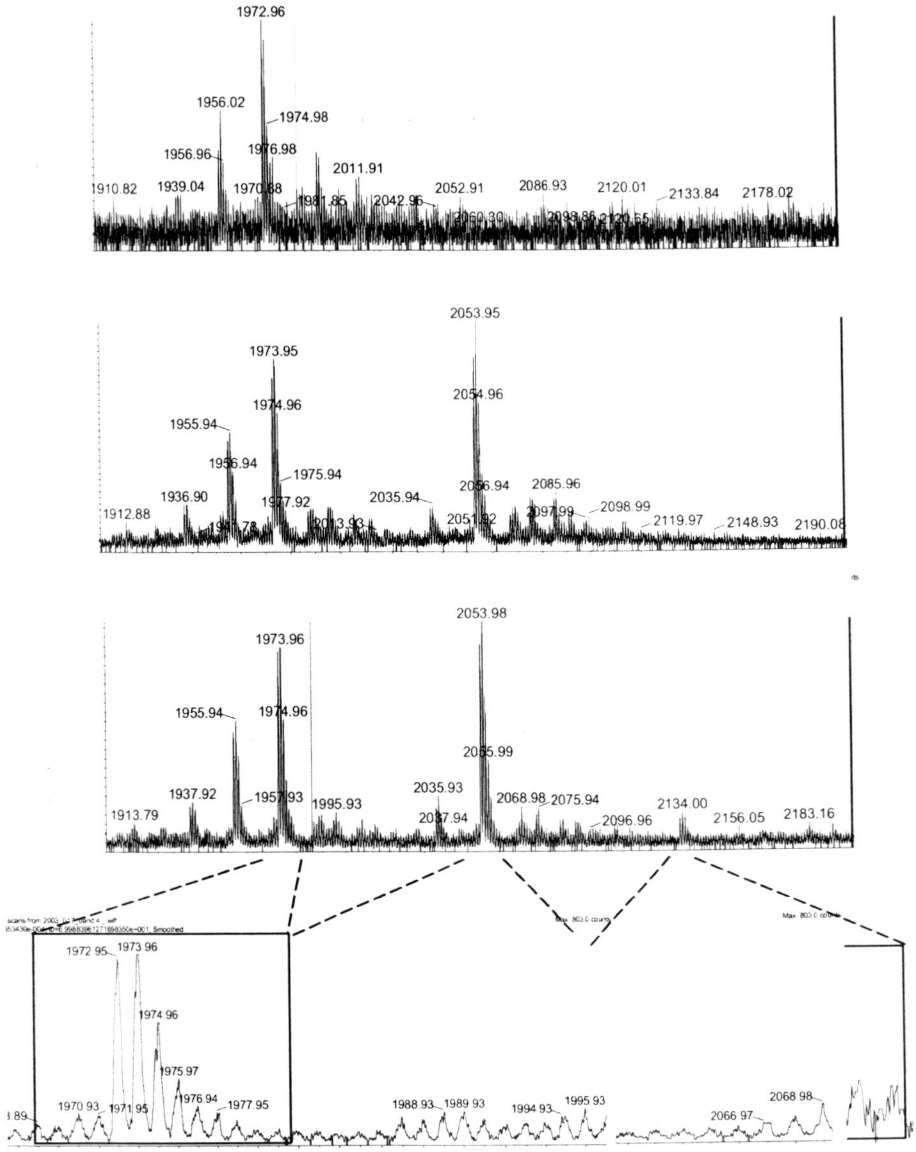

Figure 6. Negative ionisation mode orthogonal MALDI hybrid Q-TOF PMF analysis of MIA IEF bands I, IIa & III Details from lower panel show the resolved isotopic clusters of MIA tryptic fragment 59-76 with no, one and two +80 Da modifications (left, middle and right panel)

(4d) Whereas MS/MS analysis of the +80 Da peptide would seem the most straightforward approach to locate the exact position of the modification involved, this did not yield the results hoped for. As it turns out, the selected modified peptide is so labile that it readily loses its +80 Da moiety in the collision chamber, with no +80 Da containing fragments remaining in the rest of the spectrum.

The poor stability of the +80 Da ions observed in the above MS analyses again argues in favor of a sulfation to be responsible for the +80 Da modification, rather than a phosphorylation [19].

The charge difference between bands IIa and III is likely to be the consequence of one and two sulfations, respectively.

A minor extra band (designated IIb) discernible between band IIa and III in some preparations (see Fig. 4) is likely the result of an additional modification in a different part of the MIA molecule. A deamidation, for instance, would result in a charge shift similar to the one observed. Since this band represents only a minor fraction of the four isoforms viz. 0.3% by densitometry analysis, it was not further investigated.

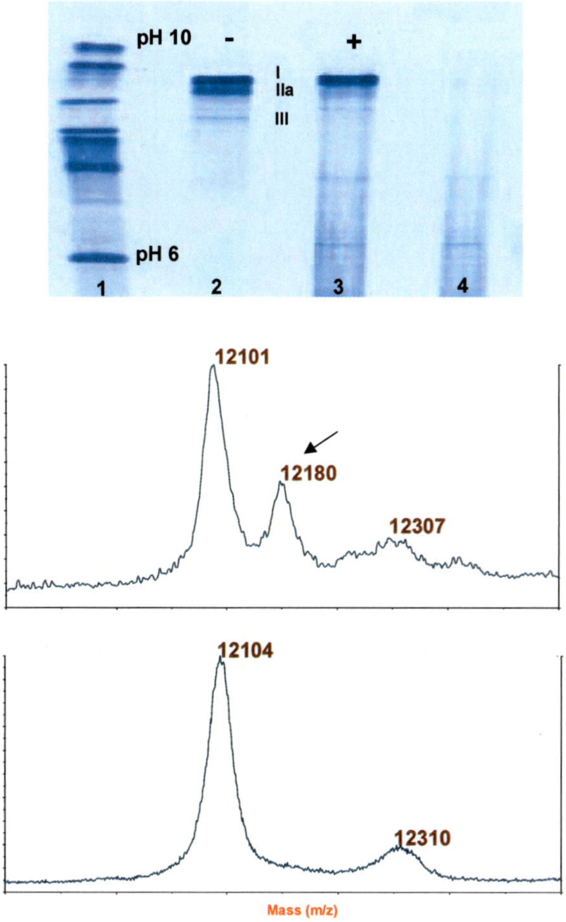

Figure 7. MALDI and IEF analysis of aryl sulfatase-treatment of MIA

A. IEF of aryl sulfatase-treated and untreated MIA. Lane 1: Serva 3-10 IEF marker; lane 2: untreated MIA; lane 3: MIA treated with aryl sulfatase. Dissappearance of bands II and III indicate removal of the +80 Da moiety by the sulfatase; lane 4: aryl sulfatase per se.

B. MALDI spectra of untreated and treated MIA shown in upper and lower trace respectively. Unmodified and +80 Da containing huMIA (arrow) appear as m/z peaks 12101 Da and 12180 Da respectively; additional higher m/z peaks are the result of sinapinnic acid adduct formation. Lower panel shows disappearance of the +80 Da signal after sulfatase treatment.

Additional Studies on the Modification of MIA

Experiments including NMR and BIA studies aiming to assess whether the observed 80 Da shift could be attributed to phosphorylation, were both negative.

In NMR studies, no ^{31}P-nuclei were detected in the recorded spectrum suggesting that MIA protein was not phosphorylated to a detectable level. Furthermore, rec MIA was not bound to a significant extent (1.7% of the theoretical value) by a monoclonal anti-phosphotyrosine antibody in a Biacore experiment, in contrast with a tyr-phosphorylated control peptide (which was bound to a level of 70% under the same conditions).

Together, these data indicate that rec huMIA is not phosphorylated on tyrosine residues.

The most straightforward way to determine whether the +80 Da PTM of MIA comprises a sulfation, is treatment with arylsulfatase and subsequent product analysis by MALDI-TOF-MS and IEF [24].

The MALDI-TOF spectra of the untreated recMIA showed the expected peaks at m/z 12101 (+/- 10 Da, corresponding to non-modified MIA) and at m/z 12180 (+80 Da modified MIA). In contrast, treatment of MIA with arylsulfatase resulted in disappearance of the +80 Da peak (Fig. 7B). In IEF analysis, untreated rec huMIA yielded the characteristic three major MIA isoforms (Fig. 7A lane 2), whereas enzyme-treated MIA lacked the more acidic bands (Fig. 7A lane 3).

In order to obtain additional evidence for Tyr-O-sulfation, MIA-producing CHO transfectants were grown in the presence of chlorate which is known to block Tyr-O-sulfation by inhibiting tyrosyl protein sulfotransferase [22,25]. The rec huMIA produced under these conditions was purified and analyzed as described above.

MALDI MS analysis of rec huMIA from cells grown in the absence of chlorate yielded peaks at m/z 12108 and 12187, corresponding with non-sulfated and sulfated MIA respectively (Fig. 8A upper panel). In contrast, cells cultured in the presence of chlorate showed a single peak at m/z 12101 (Fig. 8A lower panel).

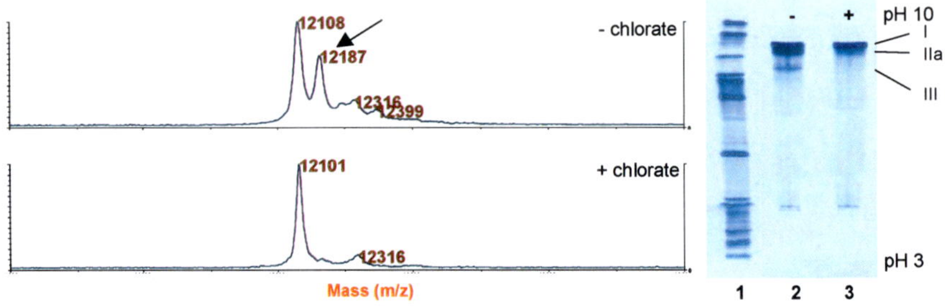

Figure 8. MALDI and IEF analysis of huMIA produced in absence and presence of chlorate
A. MALDI spectra of MIA produced in the absence or presence of chlorate are shown in upper and lower panels respectively. Arrow points to MIA + 80 Da m/z peak.
B. IEF analysis. Lane 1: Serva 3-10 IEF marker, lane 2 MIA produced in absence of chlorate, lane 3: MIA produced in presence of chlorate. In the latter preparation bands IIa and III have disappeared.

In addition, IEF analysis of MIA produced in the absence of chlorate revealed the three major characteristic rec huMIA isoforms I-III (Fig. 8B lane 2), whereas MIA produced in the presence of chlorate showed an IEF pattern that lacked the more acidic isoforms (Fig. 8B lane 3), corroborating the previous findings that these isoforms represent Tyr-O-sulfated MIA.

Discussion and Conclusion

The MS and biochemical data presented in this paper support the conclusion that part of rec huMIA produced recombinantly in CHO cells is post-translationally modified by sulfation of tyrosine residues 69 and 70. The charge difference between bands IIa and III is likely to be the consequence of one and two sulfations, respectively.

We would like to emphasize that the substoichiometric sulfation of MIA, viz. approximately 25% as estimated from IEF analyses, does not necessarily reflect the stoichiometry *in vivo*. Incomplete sulfate ester modification of recombinant proteins expressed in CHO cells has been reported by several authors [33,34]. In order to study the extent of Tyr-O-sulfation of MIA *in vivo*, the protein should be purified from natural sources like serum or synovial fluid. However, MIA concentrations range between 10 and 30 μg/L in these biological fluids [11], which is almost prohibitive for the isolation of sufficient amounts of pure, native huMIA.

Sulfation of proteins is less often described than protein phosphorylation. Nevertheless, it is a common PTM, occurring on as much as 1% of all tyrosine residues of total protein in an organism [26]. It is one of the last modifications to occur on proteins transiting the trans-Golgi and thus has been found almost exclusively on secreted and plasma membrane proteins, and this in all metazoan species examined. The modification is present usually at the interface of interacting proteins and is known to modulate extracellular protein/protein and protein/carbohydrate interactions, generally resulting in a substantially increased binding potency. Examples are hirugen/ thrombin [27], heparin cofactorII/heparin [28] and Factor VIII/ von Willebrandt factor interaction [22]. Furthermore, Tyr-(O)-sulfation has been implicated in intracellular protein transport, proteolytic processing (e.g. gastrin processing) and is important in the proteolytical activation of proteins involved in coagulation [25,29,30].

In a recent paper by Bosserhoff *et al.* [8] it is claimed that MIA shares significant structural homology with the fibronectin binding pockets of the $\alpha4\beta1$ and $\alpha5\beta1$ integrins and that MIA is, therefore, able to mask the respective epitopes on ECM molecules. However, the homology turns out to be poor (i.e. well below 20%) and modeling of the putatively homologous sequences in a PDB structure of $\alpha5\beta3$ integrin (67% similarity with $\alpha5\beta1$ integrin) [31,32] failed to demonstrate any structural resemblance between MIA and the integrins. Moreover, our studies on the binding kinetics of huMIA and fibronectin reveal an interaction of low affinity with fast on/ fast off characteristics. In our opinion it is highly unlikely, that these binding kinetics could explain the results found by other groups using prokaryotic material in an ELISA-like setting. These arguments make the conclusions of Bosserhoff *et al.* [8] less likely.

Lougheed *et al.* point at the resemblance of the MIA amino acid sequence ^{66}QGDYYGDLAAR^{77} (extruding from the proten moiety in the published 3D structure [2-4, 12]) with the YGYYGDALR sequence in laminin that has been implicated in recognition of $\alpha2\beta1$ integrin. However, as these studies were performed with *E. coli* produced MIA (to our knowledge no cases of tyrosine sulfation in prokaryotes have been reported), they did not take into account the consequences of a possible Tyr-(O)-sulfation at this particular site which might change the interaction properties of the distal loop dramatically.

We would like to emphasize here that all essential investigations up to now on structure and function of human MIA have been carried out with protein produced by *E. coli* (denatured and refolded from inclusion bodies). Preliminary NMR experiments on the 3D structure of CHO-produced huMIA suggest a different folding of the protein as compared with the prokaryote product. The present data show that recombinant huMIA protein can be Tyr-O-sulfated but it remains to be established that these data are equivalent in native huMIA. In the latter case it may be speculated that O-tyrosine sulfation of huMIA is a key factor in its biological activity. The postulated metastasis-promoting activity of MIA *in vivo* could be mediated through an as yet unknown factor via Tyr-(O)-sulfation enhanced binding kinetics.

This might imply that, at least, part of the experiments on the function of MIA should be repeated with eukaryotic material and that studies on the effects of tyrosine sulfation on MIA binding and biological activity should be included. Furthermore, resolving the 3D structure of CHO-produced huMIA, either by X-ray crystallography or by NMR, may contribute to a correct interpretation of the *in vitro* and *in vivo* experiments at the molecular level.

ACKNOWLEDGEMENTS

The authors are much indebted to H. Schellekens for performing the cloning experiments, W. Koot for cell culture experiments, Dr. C. Kloks for performing the NMR analysis, M. Bruisten for protein purification and D. Vu-Pham for carrying out the IEF analysis. Dr. M.-J. van Lierop is acknowledged for carrying out the MIA *in vitro* assays and for valuable discussions. We thank Dr. A. Garritsen for critical reading of the manuscript.

REFERENCES

[1] Bosserhoff, A.K.; Buettner, R. *Histol. Histopathol.* 2002 17, 289-300.

[2] Stoll, R.; Renner, C.; Zweckstetter, M.; Brueggert, M.; Ambrosius, D.; Palme, S.; Engh, R.A.; Golob, M.; Breibach, I.; Buettner, R.; Voelter, W.; Holak, T.A.; Bosserhoff, A.K. *EMBO J.* 2001 20, 340-349.

[3] Lougheed, J.C.; Domaille, P.; Handel, T.M. *J. Biomol. NMR* 2002 22, 211-223.

[4] Lougheed, J.C.; Holton, J.M.; Alber, T.; Bazan, J.F.; Handel, T.M. *Proc. Natl. Acad. Sci.* USA 2001 98, 5515-5520.

[5] Blesch, A.; Bosserhoff, A.K.; Apfel, R.; Behl, C.; Hessdoerfer, B.; Schmitt, A.; Jachlmczak, P.; Lottspeich, F.; Buettner, R.; Bogdahn, U. *Cancer Res.* 1994 54, 5695-5701.

[6] Van Groningen, J.J.; Bloemers, H.P.; Swart, G.W. *Cancer Res.* 1995 55, 6237-6243.

[7] Guba, M.; Bosserhoff, A.K.; Steinbauer, M.; Abels, C.; Anthuber, M.; Buettner R.; Jauch, K.W. Brit. *J. Cancer* 2000 83, 1216-1222.

[8] Bosserhoff, A.K.; Stoll, R.; Sleeman, J.P.; Bataille, F.; Buettner, R.; Holak, T.A. *Laboratory Investigation* 2003 83, 1583-1594.

[9] Bosserhoff, A.K.; Golob, M.; Buettner, R.; Landthaler, M.; Hein R. Hautarzt 1998 49, 762-769.

[10] Bosserhoff, A.K.; Buettner, R. *Biomaterials* 2003 24, 3229-3234.

[11] Saito, S.; Kondo, S.; Mishima, N.; Ishiguro, Y.; Hasegawa, L.; Sandell, J.; Iwata H. J. *Bone Joint Surg*. 2002 84-B, 1066-1069.

[12] Stoll, R.; Renner, C.; Buettner, R.; Voelter, W.; Bosserhoff, A.K.; Holak, T.A. Protein *Science* 2003 12, 510-519.

[13] Neuhoff, V.; Stamm, R.; Eibl, H. *Electrophoresis* 1985 6, 427-448.

[14] Bogdahn, U.; Buettner, R; Kaluza, B. European Patent 1999 *EP* 0 710 248 B1.

[15] BIAtechnology Handbook, *Pharmacia Biosensor*, Ed. 1994

[16] Annan, R.S.; Carr, S. *Anal Chem*. 1996 68, 3413-3421.

[17] Nemeth-Cawley, J.F.; Karnik, S.; Rouse, J.C. *J. Mass Spect*. 2001 36, 1301-1311.

[18] Harvey, D.J.; Hunter, A.P.; Bateman, R.H.; Brown, J.; Critchley, G. *Int. J. Mass Spectrom*. 1999 188, 131-146.

[19] Rappsilber, J.; Steen, H.; Mann, M. *J. Mass Spectrom*. 2001 36, 832-833.

[20] Wolfender, J.L.; Chu, F.; Ball, H.; Wolfender, F.; Fainzilber, M.; Baldwin, M.A.; Burlingame, A.L. *J. Mass Spectrom*. 1999 34, 447-454.

[21] Wirth, U.; Mueller, D.; Schindler, P.; Lange, J.; van Oostrum, *J. Proteomics* 2002 2, 1445-1451.

[22] Pittman, D.D.; Wang, J.H.; Kaufman, R.J. *Biochemistry* 1992 31, 3315-3325.

[23] Dong, J.; Li, C.Q.; Lopez, J.A. *Biochemistry* 1994 33, 13946-13953.

[24] Cimino, C.O.; Shelmutt, S.R.; Ronis, M.J.J.; Badger, T.M. *Clin. Chim. Acta* 1999 287, 69-82.

[25] Kehoe, J.W.; Bertozzi, C.R. *Chemistry and Biology* 2000 7, R57-R61.

[26] Huttner, W.B. *Ann. Rev. Physiol*. 1988 50, 363-376.

[27] Skrzypzcak-Jankun, E.; Carperos, V.; Ravichandran, K.G.; Tulinsky, A. *J. Mol. Biol*. 1991 221, 1379-1393.

[28] Boehme, C.; Nimtz, M.; Grabenhorst, E.; Conradt, H.S.; Strathmann, A.; Ragg, H. *Eur. J. Biochem*. 2002 269, 977-988.

[29] Niehrs, C.; Beisswanger, R.; Huttner, W.B. *Chem. Biol. Interact*. 1994 92, 257-271.

[30] Moore, K.L. *J. Biol. Chem*. 2003 278, 27, 24243-24246.

[31] Xiong, J.-P.; Stehle, T.; Diefenbach, B.; Zhang, R.; Dunker, R.; Scott, D.L.; Joachimiak, A.; Goodman, S.L.; Arnaout, M.A. *Science* 2001 294, 339-345.

[32] Xiong, J.P.; Stehle, T.; Zhang, R.; Joachimiak, A.; Frech, M.; Goodman, S.L.; Arnaout, M.A. *Science* 2002 296, 151-155.

[33] Mikkelsen, J.; Thomson, J.; Ezban, M. *Biochemistry* 1991, 1533-1537.

[34] White, G.C.; Beebe, A.; Nielsen, B. Thromb. *Haemost*. 1997 78, 261-265.

In: Principles of Biomacromolecular Mass Spectrometry ISBN 1-60021-063-5
Editor: Simone Koenig, pp. 75-84

Chapter 4

MASS SPECTROMETRY IDENTIFIES HOMOLOGUES OF PHASIN PHAP1 PROTEIN OF *RALSTONIA EUTROPHA* ON POLYHYDROXYBUTYRATE GRANULES

Martin Zeller*[1], Markus Pötter*[2], Frank Reinecke[2], Alexander Steinbüchel[2], William I. Burkitt[3], Peter J. Derrick[3], and Simone König[1]

[1]Integrated Functional Genomics, Interdisciplinary Center for Clinical Research, Medical Faculty
[2]Institute for Molecular Microbiology and Biotechnology, University of Münster, Germany;
[3]Institute of Mass Spectrometry, University of Warwick, UK
* MZ and MP share first-authorship.

ABSTRACT

Many prokaryotes use polyhydroxyalkanoates (PHA) as storage compounds for carbon and/or energy in the form of water-insoluble inclusion PHA granules in the cytoplasm. The surface of such granules is covered by proteins which also affect their form and structure. Here, phasin PhaP1 protein was identified in high abundance on the grana surface of *R. eutropha* employing gel electrophoretic separation and mass spectrometry. Homologous phasins PhaP3 and Pha4 were visualized using 2D-PAGE in the PhaP1 knock-out mutant, but no evidence for the presence of PhaP2 could be found. All detected phasins exhibit isoforms whose structural differences are still a matter of investigation, although C-terminally truncated isoforms of PhaP1 were detected with FTICR-MS.

Keywords: *Mass spectrometry, protein analysis, PhaP homologues, FTICR*

---

[1] Address correspondence to: PD Dr. Simone König, Integrated Functional Genomics, Röntgenstr. 21. 48149 Münster, Germany. ph: +49-(0)251-8357164. fax: +49-(0)251-8357255. e-mail: koenigs@uni-muenster.de

Abbreviations

2D-PAGE	two-dimensional gel electrophoresis
FTICR	Fourier-transform ion cyclotron resonance
FWHM	full width at half maximum
MS	mass spectrometry
MW	molecular weight
m/z	mass/charge
NanoESI	nano electrospray
PHAs	polyhydroxyalkanoates
PhaP	phasin
PHB	poly 3-hydroxybutyrate
pI	isoelectric point

Introduction

A large variety of prokaryotes use polyhydroxyalkanoates as storage compounds for carbon and/or energy in the form of water-insoluble inclusions PHA granules in the cytoplasm. Due to their biodegradability and origin from renewable resources, PHAs have attracted much interest, and many technical and medical applications have been developed in the last few decades [1-3]. The Gram-negative facultative chemolithoautotrophic hydrogen bacterium *Ralstonia eutropha* is most probably the best studied microorganism with regard to the metabolism of polyhydroxyalkanoic acids. *R. eutropha* belongs to those bacteria which accumulate polyoxoesters of various short carbon-chain-length hydroxyalkanoic acids comprising three to five carbon atoms [4, 5]. PHAs are produced in the form of lipophilic inclusion bodies, the so-called grana which contain approximately 97.5 % PHA, 2 % protein, and 0.5 % phospholipid [6], although some estimates on the lipid contents are considerably higher [7].

Interestingly, a completely different type of PHA with a yet unknown function occurs ubiquitarily, i.e. in prokaryotes and eukaryotes, but contributes only 0.1 % of the cell matter or less. These PHA molecules exhibit a much lower molecular weight of up to ~15 kDa, and they are located in the cytoplasmic membrane or are associated or even covalently bound to other cell constituents [8]. However, enzymes and genes involved in biosynthesis of these PHAs, which are referred to as "complexed PHAs" (cPHA) and which also occur in *R. eutropha*, have not been identified, yet.

The surface of PHA granules is covered by a 2 nm membrane. It was recognized that PHA granules contain proteins at their surface which are responsible for their structure, size and function [7]. Four different types of granule-associated proteins were found in PHA producing bacteria. These are (i) the PHA synthase (PhaC), (ii) the intracellular PHA depolymerases (PhaZi), (iii) the phasins (PhaP), and (iv) a regulator protein of the phasin expresssion (PhaR). In *R. eutropha*, it was shown that PhaC is a soluble protein in the cytoplasm, which becomes only insoluble and PHA granule bound when the cells are cultivated under conditions permissive for PHA accumulation and after the onset of PHA accumulation. This is due to the covalent linkage of the growing PHA chain to the enzyme [9-11]. In *R. eutropha*, the first two enzymes of the pathway, β-ketothiolase PhaA and acetoacetyl-CoA reductase PhaB, are found in the cytoplasm during active PHA synthesis and do not bind to the granules [12, 13]. Since the PHA operon, comprising the genes *phaA*, *phaB,* and *phaC* was cloned during the eighties, many other genes involved in PHA metabolism have been subsequently identified, and the functions of the encoded proteins were at least partially analysed. Whereas *phaC* is essential for PHA biosynthesis in *R. eutropha*, *phaA* and *phaB* can be replaced by other enzymes. Phasins are considered as by far the major protein constituents and structural proteins of the layer at the surface of the PHA granules. The structural protein, PhaP, is localized at the surface of the PHB-granules, and it is synthesized in very large quantities under storage conditions, representing as much as 5 % of the total protein [14] . PhaP adheres very tightly to native as well as to artificial poly 3-hydroxybutyrate (PHB) granules. In *Rhodococcus ruber*, the anchoring region was located at the carboxy terminus; and it was demonstrated that phasin molecules truncated at the carboxy terminal region lost their capability to bind to PHA granules [15].

PHA granules can be generated *in vitro* simply by incubating purified PHA synthase protein and a suitable substrate. The addition of phasins accelerates the PHA synthesis rate. Furthermore, the size of these inclusions can be regulated by the addition of PhaP, although electron microscopic studies revealed that the granules do not have the same surface structure as native inclusions [16].

R. eutropha H16 produces PHB in the cytoplasma under certain conditions (lack of nitrogen-sources and at the same time excess of a carbon-source such as fructose). PHB is biodegradable, thermoplasctically deformable and suited for usage as packing material on an industrial scale [17, 18]. The currently available genome sequence of *R. eutropha* H16 revealed three homologues (PhaP2, PhaP3, Pha4) to the phasin protein PhaP described previously [14]. Phasins are between 14 and 28 kDa in size and form a layer at the surface of the hydrophobic core of the PHB granules with PhaP being predominant [14, 19]. PhaP1. PhaP2, PhaP3, and PhaP4 exhibit 42, 49, and 45 % identity or 61, 62, and 63 % similarity to PhaP1, respectively [20]. Phasins influence the number and size of PHB granules [14, 15, 21]. In this work, proteomic analysis of the isolated and solubilised grana of the *R. eutropha* wild-type and a PhaP1 knock-out was performed to determine, if the homologous phasins are also located at the grana surface.

Materials and Methods

PhaP1 from *R. eutropha* was isolated from native granules of fructose-grown cells of *R. eutropha* as described by [14]. The preparation of the native granules from *R. eutropha* strain H16 and the *phaP1* negative mutant *R. eutropha* Re1052 [22], solubilization of the granule-associated proteins, and their separation using 2D-PAGE is described in ref. [20].

For testing *in vivo* phasin phosphorylation cells were cultivated in the presence of ^{32}P-phosphoric acid (500 µCi) in a phosphorous-poor Tris-based mineral salts medium [23]. Granule proteins were prepared as above and the corresponding 2D-gel was dried on filter paper using a vacuum gel slab dryer at 60°C for four hours. The dried gel was covered with a thin cling film and photographic film was placed on top for several days.

For protein identification, spots of interest were cut out of the gel, washed and tryptically digested according to a procedure slightly modified from ref. [24]. Peptides were extracted and purified using ZipTips C18 (Millipore, Bedford, MA, USA). Peptide maps were generated using TofSpec-2E instrument (Micromass, Manchester, UK) in reflectron mode. Data analysis was performed with Mascot (MatrixScience, London, UK) in-house searching a proprietary *R. eutropha* database. Isoforms were scrutinized manually.

For FTICR, lyophilised sample of PhaP1 purified from *R. eutropha* wild-type (10 µmol in 100 mM Tris according to Bradford test) was reconstituted with 100 µl destilled water. 10 µl was acidified with 2 µl formic acid and desalted using ZipTips C4 into 10 µl 70 % acetonitrile containing 0.1 % acetic acid. After dilution with 10 µl 0.1 % acetic acid FTICR experiments were carried out on a BioAPEX-94e mass spectrometer with a passively shielded 9.4 Tesla magnet and a standard hexapole-based interface (Analytica of Branford, MA, USA). For nanoelectrospray [25] metal-coated glass capillaries from Protana (Protana, Odense, Denmark) were used. The *m/z* scale was externally calibrated with an Agilent calibrant.

RESULTS AND DISCUSSION

2D-PAGE was employed to separate the phasin proteins in crude cell extracts or poly(3HB) granules (Fig. 1). Difficulties due to the similarities in the MWs of the proteins (Table 1) had to be observed and, therefore, pH gradient strips 5-8 were used for better resolution. PhaP1 occurs in large amounts (appproximately 5 % of the protein content under storage conditions) in the wild-type preventing the detection of phasins present in lower amounts. Three spots were resolved in the 2D-PAGE experiment of the wild-type strain, which could be all assigned to PhaP1 (Fig. 1a). Fig. 2 shows the peptide maps of the left and the right spot the spectrum of the middle spot being fairly identical with that of the left spot. As is highlighted in Fig. 3, signals for 91 % of the expected sequence could be found for the intense spots. For the fainter right spot still 62 % of the sequence were assigned. In both left spots most peptide peaks were accompanied by signals 57 and 75 Da higher in mass. It remains to be clarified what modification or contamination was responsible for that effect and if it caused any shift in protein pI. No evidence for the addition of hydroxy butyric acid derivatives could be found but phosphorylation was considered. Due to the introduction of additional negative charges by phosphorylation proteins shift towards a more acidic pI on the gel. This effect has been successfully employed for comparative phosphoproteomics based on enzymatic dephosphorylation [26].

Table1: GenBank entries for phasin homologues

accession number	phasin	MW	pI
AAC78327	PhaP1	19966,54	5,96
AAP85954	PhaP2	20223,04	5,95
AY489113	PhaP3	19595,94	6,12
AY489114	PhaP4	20183,85	5,91

To check for phosphorylation, two approaches were followed in parallel. *In vivo* phosphorylation of phasins was questioned by cultivation of cells in the presence of ^{32}P-phosphoric acid in a phosphorous-poor Tris-based mineral salt medium [23]. However, no signals were observed in the phasing region.

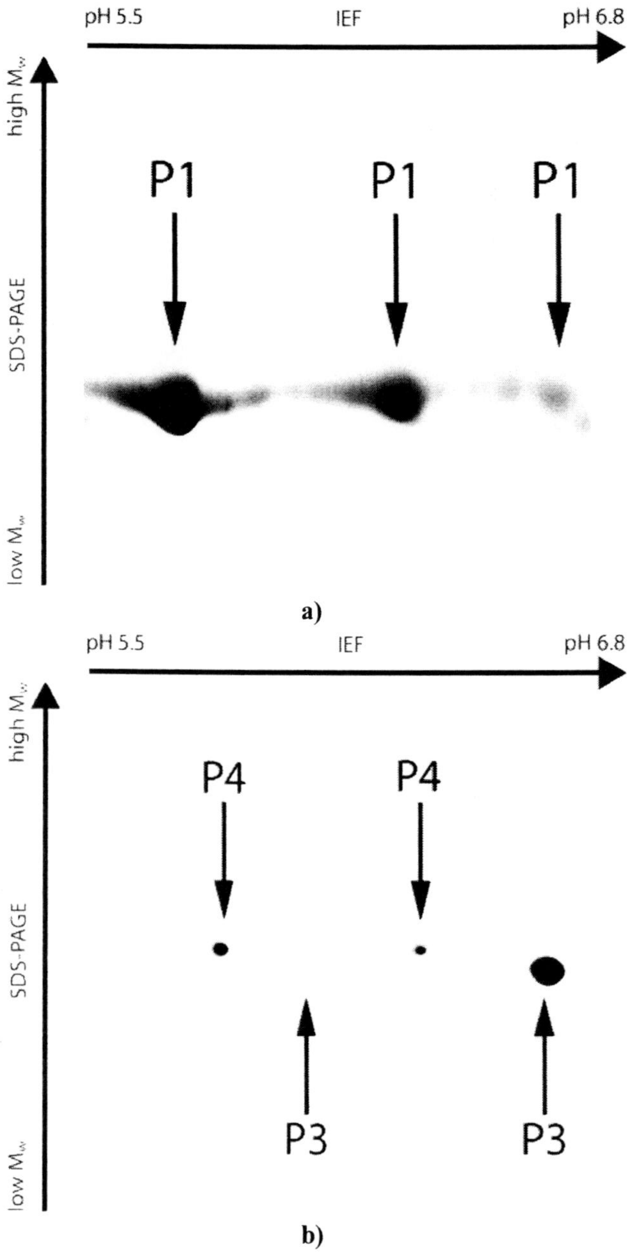

Figure 1: Gel images of the separated phasing homologues of a) *R. eutropha* wild-type; b) knock-out mutant *ΔphaP1*. Sections of the gel photographs presented in ref. [20]

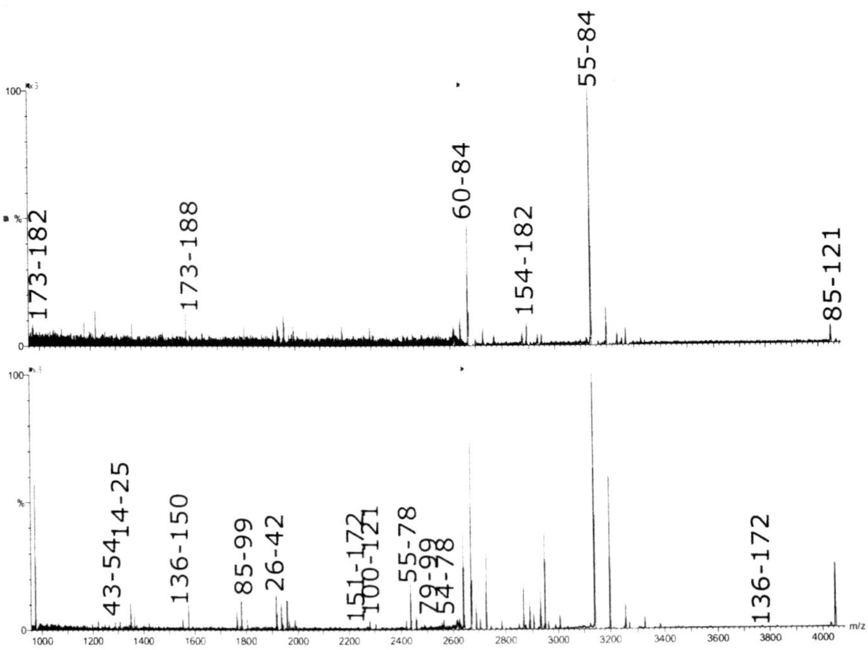

Figure 2: Peptide maps (relative intensity *versus m/z*) of PhaP1-spots shown in Fig. 1a. Top trace: Right-most spot showing lowest abundance. Bottom trace: abundant left spot. Signals labeled with the corresponding amino acid residues. See Fig. 3.

1 MILTPEQVAA AQKANLETLF GLTTKAFEGV EKLVELNLQV
41 VKTSFAEGVD NAKKALSAKD AQELLAIQAA AVQPVAEKTL
81 AYTRHLYEIA SETQSEFTKV AEAQLAEGSK NVQALVENLA
121 KNAPAGSEST VAIVKSAISA ANNAYESVQK ATKQAVEIAE
161 TNFQAAATAA TKAAQQASAT ARTATAKKTT AA

Figure 3: PhaP1 sequence showing assignments of peptide maps in Fig. 2. Underlined: Fig. 1a right spot, spectrum Fig. 2 top trace. Italicized: Fig. 1a left spot, spectrum Fig. 2 bottom trace.

In a second approach high resolution nanoESI-FTICR-MS [27] was used to determine the molecular weights of the intact phasin wild-type proteins [28-30]. With this technique it was expected to both find modifications of PhaP1 *R. eutropha* wild-type and any of the homologous isoforms PhaP2-4 which could be present as minor compounds due to the purification protocol [14]. Fig 4a shows the nanoESI-FTICR mass spectrum with a zoom-in on the 14+ peak of PhaP1 in Fig. 4b. Approximately 250 scans were accumulated. The resolution ($m/\Delta m_{FWHM}$) of the peaks is > 100.000 and the isotopic peaks are baseline-resolved which is a prerequisite for the exact mass determination. The peaks for the different charge states of the proteins all have satellites indicating methionine oxidation which is likely caused by sample handling. Since there is only one Met in the PhaP1 sequence at the N-terminus, the other protein species were expected to be either other phasins or C-terminally modified PhaP1 [1-192] (Table 2). Predominant in the spectrum are the peaks for PhaP1 [1-192] in the charge states 16+ to 12+. Minor peaks could be assigned to PhaP1 [1-190] and [1-182]. There is also evidence for the presence of PhaP1 [1-184] and [1-115]. However, no signals for PhaP2-4 or phosphorylation of any of the species were detected (Table 3).

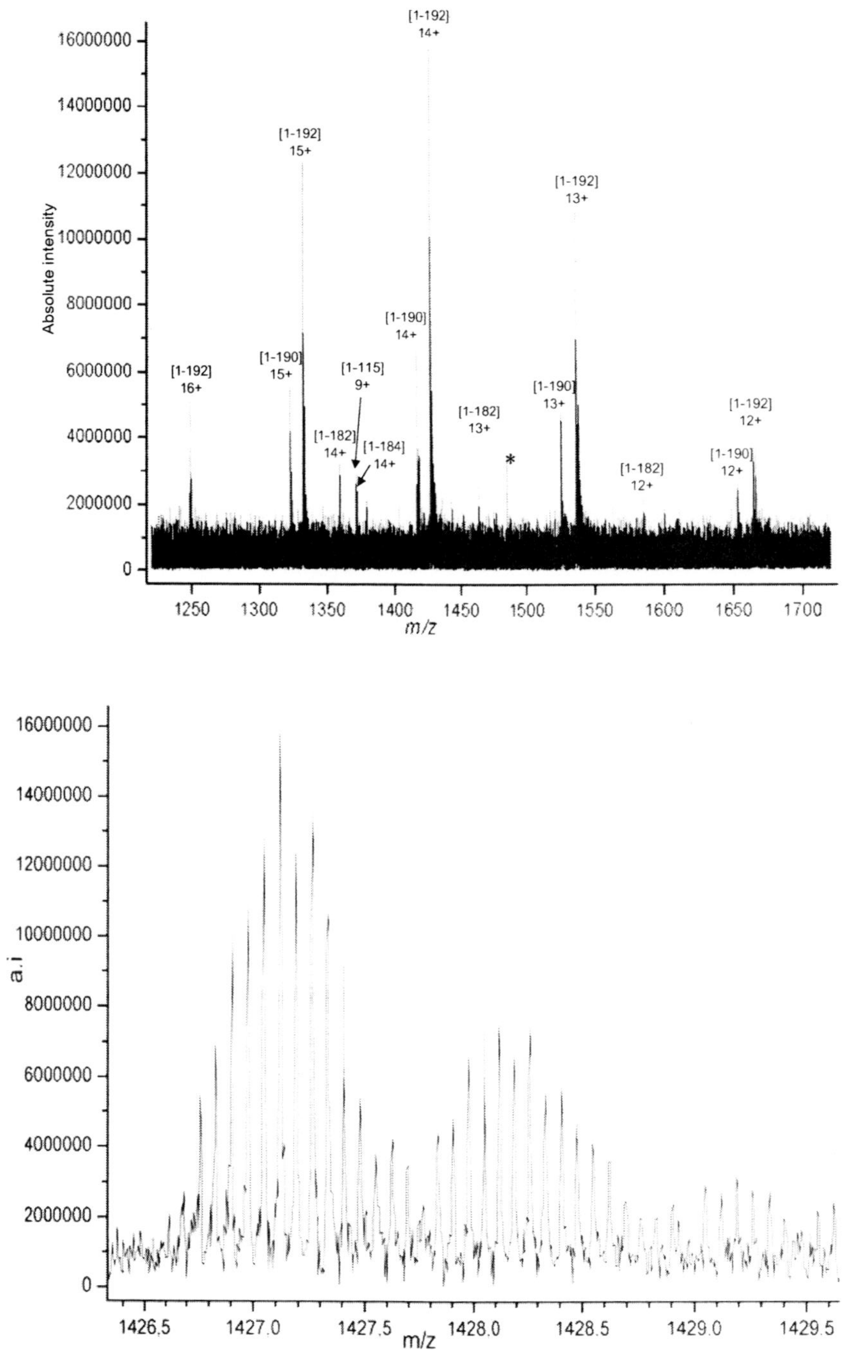

Figure 4: a) NanoESI-FTICR mass spectrum of PhaP1. b) Zoom in on the +14-charge state. (* denotes a spike)

Table 2: Assignment of most abundant isotopomere FTICR peaks observed the PhaP1 preparation

$[^{13}C_{11}{}^{32}S_1]$ PhaP1 [1-192]			
Charge state	Observed mass (m/z)	Calculated mass (m/z)	Δ ppm
+ 12	1664,81220	1664,80273	5,68
+ 13	1536,82294	1536,81852	2,88
+ 14	1427,12073	1427,11776	2,08
+ 15	1332,04555	1332,04376	1,34
+ 16	1248,85536	1248,85401	1,08
$[^{13}C_{11}{}^{32}S_1]$ PhaP1 [1-190]			
Charge state	Observed mass (m/z)	Calculated mass (m/z)	Δ ppm
+ 12	1652,96790	1652,96323	2,82
+ 13	1525,89299	1525,88973	2,14
+ 14	1416,97200	1416,96960	1,69
+ 15	1322,58153	1322,57215	7,09
$[^{13}C_{11}{}^{32}S_1]$ PhaP1 [1-182]			
Charge state	Observed mass (m/z)	Calculated mass (m/z)	Δ ppm
+ 12	1586,09909	1586,09198	4,48
+ 13	1464,08756	1464,08529	1,00
+ 14	1359,58219	1359,57976	1,79

Table 3: MWs (calculated according to ref. [32]).and pIs for the PhaP1 isoforms detected with FTICR

Amino acid residues	MW (average)	pI
[1-192]	19967	6,0
[1-190]	19825	6,0
[1-184]	19194	5,3
[1-182]	19022	5,3
[1-115]	12333	5,0

The FTICR results do not offer an explanation for the pI shift, since peptides were found in all three maps up to amino acid residue 188. While the suggested loss of the two C-terminal alanines might be possible according to the above experimental results, it should not cause a pI shift because their side chains do not carry charges. It is evident that differences in sample preparation need to be investigated.

Was the abundant PhaP1 protein knocked-out in mutant Δ*phaP1*, 2D-PAGE demonstrated the presence of PhaP3 and PhaP4 beside BktB and GroEL in the granule proteome (Fig. 1b) [20]. OPhaP2 was not detected here, although others showed its synthesis in *R. eutropha* [31].

CONCLUSION

PhaP1 protein was identified in high abundance on the grana surface of *R. eutropha*. Homologous phasins PhaP3 and Pha4 could be visualized on 2D-PAGE in the PhaP1 knock-out mutant. No evidence for the presence of PhaP2 was found in these experiments. All detected phasins exhibit isoforms whose structural differences are still a matter of investigation, although C-terminally truncated isoforms of PhaP1 were detected with FTICR-MS.

ACKNOWLEDGMENTS

M. Zeller was funded by a Marie Curie Training Fellowship of the European Union. Studies on PhaP1 and other phasins were founded by the Deutsche Forschungsgemeinschaft (Ste386/6-2) and by the German Federal Ministry of Education and Research (BMBF) within the framework of the Competence Network Göttingen "Genome research on bacteria (GenoMik). We thank A. J. Sinskey (MIT, Cambridge, USA) for providing the *R. eutropha* strain Re1052.

This work is part of the PhD-theses of M. Zeller, M. Pötter, and F. Reinecke.

REFERENCES

[1] Anderson, A. J., Dawes, E. *A. Microbiol. Rev.* 1990, 54, 450-472.

[2] Hocking, P. J., Marchessault, R. H. Biopolyesters. *In Chemistry and Technology of Biodegradable Polymers;* Chapman and Hall: London, 1994.

[3] Williams, S. F., Martin, D. P. *In Biopolymers*; Doi, Y., Steinbüchel A., Ed.; WILEY-VCH: Weinheim, 2002; Vol. 4 (Polyesters III - Applications and commercial products), pp 91-127.

[4] Schlegel, H. G., Gottschalk, G., Bartha, V. *Nature* 1961, 29, 463-465.

[5] Steinbüchel, A., Valentin, H. E. *FEMS Microbiol. Lett.* 1995, 128, 219-228.

[6] Griebel, R., Smith, Z., Merrick, J.M. *Biochemistry* 1968, 7, 3676-3681.

[7] Steinbüchel, A., Aerts, K., Babel, W., Föllner, C., Liebergesell, M., Madkour, M. H., Mayer, F., Pieper-Fürst, U., Pries, A., Valentin H. E., Wieczorek, R. Can. *J. Microbiol.* 1995, 41, Suppl. 1, 94-105.

[8] Reusch, R. N. In Polyesters I - *Biological systems and biotechnological production*; WILEY-VCH: Weinheim, 2002; Vol. 3A, pp 123-172.

[9] Gerngross, T. U., Reilly, P., Stubbe, J., Sinskey, A.J. and Peoples, O.P. J. *Bacteriol.* 1993, 175, 5289-5293.

[10] Liebergesell, M., Schmidt, B., Steinbüchel, A. *FEMS Microbiol. Lett.* 1992, 78, 227-232.

[11] Liebergesell, M., Sonomoto, K., Madkour, M., Mayer, F., Steinbüchel, A. *Eur. J. Biochem.* 1994, 226, 71-80.

[12] Haywood, H. W., Anderson, A. J., Chu, L. , Dawes, A. E. *FEMS Microbiol. Lett.* 1988, 52, 91-96.

[13] Haywood, H. W., Anderson, A. J., Chu, L. , Dawes, A. E. *FEMS Microbiol. Lett.* 1988, 52, 259-264.

[14] Wieczorek, R.; Pries, A.; Steinbüchel, A.; Mayer, F. J. *Bacteriol.* 1995, 177, 2425-2435.

[15] Pieper-Fürst, U.; Madkour, M. H.; Mayer, F.; Steinbüchel, A. J. *Bacteriol.* 1995, 177, 2513-2523.

[16] Jossek, R., Steinbüchel, A. *FEMS Microbiol. Lett.* 1998, 168, 319-324.

[17] Steinbüchel, A. *In Biomaterials*; Byrom, D., Ed.; Macmillan: Basingstoke, UK, 1991, pp 123-213.

[18] Müller, H. M.; Seebach, D. Angew. *Chem.* 1993, 105, 483-509.

[19] Pötter, M.; Madkour, M. H.; Mayer, F.; Steinbüchel, A. *Microbiology* 2002, 148, 2413-2426.

[20] Pötter, M.; Müller, H.; Reineke, F.; Wieczorek, R.; Fricke, F.; Bowien, B.; Friedrich, B.; Steinbüchel, A. *Microbiology* 2004, 150, 2301-2311.

[21] Steinbüchel, A.; Aerts, K.; Babel, W.; Follner, C.; Liebergesell, M.; Madkour, M. H.; Mayer, F.; Pieper-Fürst, U.; Pries, A.; Valentin, H. E. Can. J. *Microbiol.* 1995, 41, Suppl 1: 94-105.

[22] York, G. M., Junker, B. H. H., Stubbe, J. A., Sinskey, A. J. *J Bacteriol* 2001, 183, 4217-4226.

[23] Mergeay, M., Nies, D., Schlegel, H. G., Gerits, J., Charles, P. ,Van Gijsegem, F. J *Bacteriol.* 1985, 162, 328-334.

[24] Shevchenko, A.; Wilm, M.; Vorm, O.; Mann, M. *Anal. Chem. 1996, 68, 850-858.*

[25] Wilm, M.; Mann, M. *Anal. Chem.* 1996, 68, 1-8.

[26] Yamagata, A.; Kristensen, D. B.; Takeda, Y.; Miyamoto, Y.; Okada, K.; Inamatsu, M.; Yoshizato, K. *Proteomics* 2002, 2, 1267-1276.

[27] Palmblad, M.; Hakansson, K.; Hakansson, P.; Feng, X.; Cooper, H. J.; Giannakopulos, A. E.; Green, P. S.; Derrick, P. J. *Eur. J. Mass Spectrom.* 2000, 6, 267-275.

[28] Green, M. K.; Vestling, M. M.; Johnston, M. V.; Larsen, B. S. *Anal. Biochem.* 1998, 260, 204-211.

[29] Lafitte, D.; Heck, A. J.; Hill, T. J.; Jumel, K.; Harding, S. E.; Derrick, P. J. *Eur. J. Biochem.* 1999, 261, 337-344.

[30] Johnson, K. A.; Amster, I. J. J. *Am. Soc. Mass Spectrom.* 2001, 12, 819-825.

[31] Srinivasan, S. B., G.C.; Gerngross, T.U. *Appl. Environ. Microbiol.* 2002, 68, 5925-5932.

[32] Yergey, J. A. *Int. J. Mass Spectrom. Ion Phys.* 1983, 52, 337-349.

Münster Conference on Single Cell Analysis

Progress in Research and Technology
Münster, November 16, 2004

Organizers: Interdisciplinary Center of Clinical Research, Core Facility Integrated Functional Genomics, Münster, Germany
Clemens Sorg, Peter Josten, Kurt Sieberns, Kristina Riehemann, Simone König
Chairs: Clemens Sorg, Simone König, Hans Oberleithner, Solon Thanos

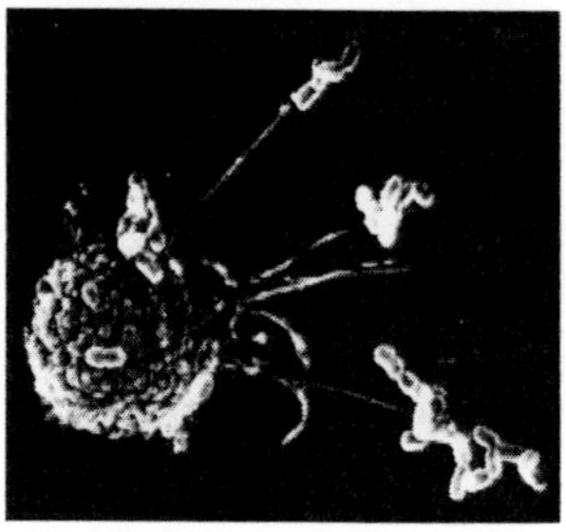

In: Principles of Biomacromolecular Mass Spectrometry ISBN 1-60021-063-5
Editor: Simone Koenig, pp. 87

Chapter 5

MASS SPECTROMETRY IN SINGLE CELL ANALYSIS

Simone König

As technologies are refined, individual cells become increasingly the focus of functional investigations and science-political interest. Mass spectrometry has only a very limited role to play in that area yet, essentially being restricted to small molecule detection and tissue imaging. However, the technique advances fast and will, therefore, be monitored in this book.

The 1st Conference on Single Cell Analysis drew much interest from scientists of very different fields. The organizing committee tried to address the broad spectrum of methods applicable to single cell or single molecule analysis so that mass spectrometry was represented only as a small part. Nevertheless, the invited contributions by Bernhard Spengler and Markus Stöckli on tissue imaging techniques created excitement among the present non-mass spectrometrists and science managers. The interplay of mass detection with peripheric techniques such as capillary electrophoresis and laser microdissection was underscored as in the presentation by Norman Dovichi. To be watched is also the "toponomics" developed by the group of Walter Schubert, a technique based on antibodies which allows protein localization with the cell environment.

While the 2004 conference was not at all comprehensive in terms of mass spectrometry applications to single cell analysis, and the pioneers in the field (see Garden et al. *J. Mass Spectrom.* 1996, 31, 10: 1126-1130; Li et al. *Anal. Chem* 1997, 69: 563-565; Chiu & Zare *PNAS* 1998, 95, 7: 3972-3977; Jiminez *et al. Biochemistry* 1998, 37, 7: 2070-2076) could not even be present, there is potential to improve on that this year. A show of hands among the participants confirmed the general feeling that monitoring progress in single cell analysis is timely and meets scientific interest. The participants called for a repetition of the conference which will take place in Münster in a larger setting in September 2005.

In: Principles of Biomacromolecular Mass Spectrometry ISBN 1-60021-063-5
Editor: Simone Koenig, pp. 89-97

Chapter 6

SPEAKER ABSTRACTS

COMPUTATIONAL SYSTEMS BIOLOGY: TOWARDS 'IN SILICO' CELL MODELS?

Hergo Holzhütter
Humboldt-University Berlin

After sequencing of complete genomes it has become apparent that single genes or their products do not cause most of the biological phenomena observed. These findings have drawn researchers to the conclusion that the most interesting phenomena in biology result from the interrelated actions of many components within the system as a whole. For elucidating and quantifying these molecular interrelations efficient high-throuput techniques have been developed to measure in parallel concentration profiles of many different mRNA's, proteins and metabolites (=molecular variables). The central problem is currently the causal interpretation of such 'molecular snapshots'. Computational systems biology is a rapidly growthing new field in biosciences that aims at formulating both molecular interactions and molecular states into mathematical models of various complexity. The final goal of this approach to set up computer models of whole cells that allow to the predict the temporal and spatial behavior of a large set of molecular variables at various external conditions (e.g. changes in temperature, pH or supply of substrates) or alterations on the molecular level (e.g. inherited enzyme defects, inhibition of processes with drugs). Currently there exist basically two alternative approaches to reach this ambitious goal. The bottom-up approach continues the traditional way of settling models on a detailed kinetic description of the underlying elementary processes. The top-down approach tries to identify and quantify the relevant interrelations among molecular variables directly from large amounts of high-troughput data. In my talk I will outline the specific strengths and weaknesses of these approaches and the role that single cell analysis may have in contributing to both of them.

The Necessity of Cell- and Cell Type-Specific Expression Analyses in Cardiopulmonary Research

Ludger Fink
Justus-Liebig-University, Giessen

The morphological study and the identification of cell differentiation within tissues are the basis for assessment of physiological and pathological processes. Applying molecular techniques, the analysis of commonly used tissue homogenates bears the risk of masking genetic deviations or expression changes of an individual cell type by the bulk of surrounding cells. To overcome the problem of tissue heterogeneity, cells have to be harvested selectively for further analysis. Therefore, microdissection techniques were developed making retrieval of target cells simple, rapid and precise. Accordingly, the use of these techniques has increased exponentially within the last few years.

Presenting three examples from cardiopulmonary research, it is demonstrated that single cell isolation is often preconditional for the investigation of splicing isoform expression (1). Combining microdissection of few cells and real-time RT-PCR allows to determine relative mRNA expression in a cell-type specific manner to reveal gene regulation (2). Combination with RNA preamplification techniques and micro arrays results in cell type- or compartment-specific expression profiles that especially differ from those of tissue homogenates when minor represented cell types are investigated (3). In consequence, the isolation of cells or cell types allows a more accurate investigation of complex tissues and gives deeper insight to regulation processes and crosstalk of the respective cells.

Immunogenetics at Single Cell Level

Jan Buer
Institute of Medical Microbiology, Hannover Medical School, Hannover & Mucosal Immunity Group, German Research Centre for Biotechnology, Braunschweig

The immune response is governed by a complex array of cellular populations and sub-population. Gene expression profiling is proving an important means of understanding and classifying physiologic and pathophysiologic processes by identifying genes, gene pathways and pathway networks not previously known to be associated with inflammation and autoimmunity. However, disease-associated gene expression can be obscured by surrounding 'normal' cells / tissue. The ability to study and compare gene usage at the cellular level will therefore provide valuable new insights into the biology of a disturbed immune response. A summary of developments in the area of expression profiling in single cells of the immune system will be described, and the rationale for these types of studies will be presented based on our own experience in studying the maintenance and break down of tolerance in both mice and humans.

Single Cell Proteomics

Norman Dovichi
University of Washington, Seattle, USA

It is now possible to generate one- and two-dimensional electrophoresis data from single mammalian cells. These separations are capable of resolving hundreds of components from the cell, and the data can be correlated with cell cycle and other properties of the cells. Examples have been generated from breast, prostate, colon, andesophageal cancer cell lines, from astrocytes and neurons, and fromosteoprecursors and myoblasts. Instrumentation is under development that can characterize tens of thousands of cells per day in one-dimensional electrophoresis and thousands of cells per day in two-dimensional electrophoresis. Related technology is under development to monitor post-translation modifications of specific proteins in single cells at the single copy level.

Higher Mass Accuracy, Higher Lateral Resolution: A Closer View of Single Cells

Bernhard Spengler, Werner Bouschen, Dieter Kirsch and Martin Köstler
Institute of Inorganic and Analytical Chemistry, Justus Liebig University, Giessen

With the combination of soft ion formation techniques and ultraprecise mass spectrometers, the accurate mass of biomolecules is becoming a physical quantity of high interest in bioanalytical methodology. FT-ICR mass spectrometry with ESI or MALDI sources now allows to easily determine the amino acid composition and sequence of medium size unknown peptides. This new method, called "Composition-based Sequencing (CBS)" [1] appears to open new perspectives in proteomics. On the single cell level, another feature of FT-ICR mass spectrometry will be of importance in the future, which is the high mass resolving power for being able to analyse highly complex, non-fractionated samples.

Investigating single cells directly by MALDI requires not only the high mass resolving power and high mass accuracy, but also a sufficient lateral focusing of the laser beam. MALDI imaging [2] is a new technique of visualizing biomolecule distributions in tissue by mass spectrometry. Most instruments developed for this approach, however, lack the necessary lateral resolution for reaching the single cell level. All of them so far lack the necessary mass resolving power and accuracy to identify and characterize proteins from single cells by this approach.

A goal for the future is to combine micrometer-resolution MALDI imaging with high accuracy FT-ICR mass spectrometry. The prospects and limitations of this approach will be discussed and first results will be presented.

[1] B. Spengler; *J. Am. Soc. Mass Spectrom.* 15 (2004) 703 - 714.
[2] B. Spengler, M. Hubert; *J. Am. Soc. Mass Spectrom.* 13 (2002) 735-748.

MALDI Mass Spectrometric Imaging Applied in the Race to Find New Cures for Diseases

Markus Stöckli
Novartis Institutes for BioMedical Research Basel

Molecular imaging techniques play an increasingly important role in biomedical research. With the ability to localize changes in organisms on the molecular level, we have a tremendous amount of information in hands to support the effort to find new cures for diseases. Widely applied molecular imaging techniques in research such as MRI and PET utilize molecular probes to report the presence of the analytes of interest in living organisms. With matrix-assisted laser desorption/ionization mass spectrometric imaging (MALDI MSI) a technique is presented which allows de-novo spatial analysis of biological samples. Sections of the tissues are introduced in mass spectrometer, where a laser is used to raster over the tissue while acquiring mass spectra of the ablated ions at every image point. From one array of spectra, hundreds of analyte-specific images can be generated, based on the selected masses. This allows a detailed tissue analysis with a resolution in the micrometer range for protein, compounds and metabolites. The techniques has been applied to target finding, biomarker discovery and drug delivery studies. Applications shown in this presentation cover different stages in biomedical research, from localization of high-mass proteins in tissue sections to drug imaging in dosed animals.

Laser Micromanipulation and Capture of Single Cells – New Approaches in Cell and Molecular Biology

Yilman Niyaz, M. Stich, B. Sägmüller, R. Gangnus, K. Schütze
P.A.L.M Microlaser Technologies AG, Bernried

The understanding of the molecular mechanisms of cellular interactions depends on identification, isolation and finally characterization of a single cell or a population of cells and thereafter of their specific subsets of biomolecules. Thus, sample generation is a very crucial step for high-resolution downstream applications. Laser Microdissection and Pressure Catapulting (LMPC) is a well-known method to isolate and collect selected cells from complex animal or plant tissues, resulting in an eminent increase in the specificity of downstream molecular analyses like PCR and RT-PCR amplification, DNA, RNA and protein microarray analysis, and MALDI/SELDI spectrometry. With LMPC, only the force of focused laser light is utilized to excise selected single cells or large tissue areas of a specimen down to a resolution of subcellular components like organelles or chromosomes, respectively. After microdissection, the separated sample is directly lifted up into an appropriate collection device by using the same laser (Laser Pressure Catapulting, LPC). As both processes are working entirely without any mechanical contact, LMPC enables pure and homogeneous sample retrieval from e.g., paraffin and cryosections, cell smears, cytospins and chromosome preparations. An important innovation is the laser driven isolation of cultured cells. The work with selected living cells is extremely facilitated with this new approach and opens a wide field of new applications and research possibilities. Individual or small groups of cultured cells can be separated by morphology or fluorescent label for direct molecular analysis, clonal expansion or re-cultivation (e.g., stem cells), creation of mixed cell populations (e.g., tissue engineering), and maintaining specific cell type ratios in mixed cultures. The efficacy of this method was recently shown by LMPC-mediated isolation of transgenic murine embryonic stem cells, which were successfully used to generate chimeric mice. Furthermore, the same laser system can be used to open the cell and nuclear membrane of living cells, or drill holes into the solid wall of plant cells. This enables new methods for microinjection of drugs or genetic material into living cells without any involvement of mechanical, chemical or viral components. In addition, the controlled fusion of different cell types becomes possible with Laser MicroBeams, as could be demonstrated for B-cell hybridoma. The applied laser wavelength of 337 nm does not affect the viability of the specimens: There is no impairment of the biological information, even after several times of catapulting and recultivation, as is shown by, e.g., Comparative Genomic Hybridization (CGH) analysis. With the specificity of LMPC, the sensitivity of downstream analyzing methods becomes a critical issue. Especially in gene expression arrays but also for protein array analysis enormous efforts have been carried out to reduce the required molecule amounts. On the one hand, biased amplification should be minimized but also biomolecule detection should become feasible below femptomolar amounts. For a proof-of-principle we extracted RNA of heat shock treated versus untreated cells, both isolated by LMPC. After one single round of T7 RNA amplification, the amplified message was hybridized on a microarray chip from Zeptosens AG (Switzerland). We could demonstrate a significant and reliable gene expression result from as few as 500 cells using the extremely sensitive planar wave-guide SensiChip^{TM} technology.

In situ proteomics Imaging: Analysing "Real World" Protein Networks within Intact Cells And Tissues

Walter Schubert
Meltec Magdeburg

The hierarchy of cell function comprises at least four distinct functional levels: genome, transcriptome, proteome, and toponome. The toponome (rule of protein arrangement) is the entirety of all proteins, protein-complexes, and protein networks traced out directly on the single cell level in the natural environment of the cells in situ (e.g. tissues). Whole cell protein-fingerprinting (WCPF/MELK) enables the quantitative mathematical description and exploration of the toponome by using large tag libraries localizing proteins (hundreds simultaneously) sub- and supracellularly.

Thereby the technology addresses the fact that each protein must be at the right time at the right place at the right concentration in a cell to interact with other proteins assembled in a spatially organized network. To encode the myriads of cellular functionalities, cells appear to having at their disposal a large, albeit finite and highly non-random repertoire of toponome units, i.e. a system of rules to construct topological hierarchies in a cell's proteome. The entirety of these toponome units represents the total functional code of a cell. The complete toponome is therefore as fundamental a data set as the genome or the proteome.

NANOBIOLOGY: FROM SINGLE MOLECULE DETECTION AND MANIPULATION TOWARDS SINGLE CELL ANALYSIS IN MICROFLUIDIC NETWORKS

Dario Anselmetti

Experimental Biophysics & Applied Nanoscience, Physics Faculty, Bielefeld University, Bielefeld Institute for BioPhysics & NanoScience (BINAS)

Our concepts to detect and analyze minute amount of substance (single molecules) via mechanical and optical schemes in order to 1) fundamentally investigate the nature and related physical mechanisms of specific biomolecular interaction and 2) to ambitiously analyze the proteome of single cells in nanofluidic microdevices (lab-on-a-chip) will be presented.

a) Specific binding of single receptor and ligand molecules can be investigated in dynamic force spectroscopy experiments by atomic force microscopy (AFM) or optical laser tweezers (OT) and give access to intermolecular forces, interaction mechanism, kinetics of the reaction and the binding energy landscape. The ability to measure inter- and intramolecular forces and elasticities under physiological conditions in biological transcriptional regulators (DNA-protein) [1-3], in bioorganic synthetized peptide-DNA systems [4] and in supramolecular guest-host systems (cation-calixarene) [5] with piconewton-, nanometer- and millisecond resolution allows investigation of single ligand-receptor interaction in a broad affinity range from $K_d=10^{-5}$-10^{-15} M at a discrimination level of single point mutations.

b) The understanding and control of cellular adhesion plays an enormous role in many applications like implantation, transplantation, tissue engineering or inflammation. Our most recent results where molecular interaction and cellular adhesion was investigated on individual cells downto the single molecule level with OT [6,7] will be presented.

c) We have recently demonstrated that periodical geometric structuring of microchannels allow separation of long DNA-fragments (with sizes > 40kbp) in less than a minute [8], a fragment size range which is rarely accessible by standard separation mechanisms in microchannels. We extended our investigations on single-molecule DNA-fragment migration by means of computer simulations [9] and exploited how such structures can be used to generate DNA separation devices based on ratchet effects. In microfluidic devices governed by conditions far from thermodynamic equilibrium unexpected migration of particles and other mechanisms such as negative mobility [10,11] have been predicted theoretically. We experimentally prove this paradox migration mechanism for the first time in a structured microfluidic device with colloidal particles in solution.

d) Our concept of single-cell analytics and the first results of our microchip-integrated separation and ultra-sensitive label-free detection of minute amounts of analyte molecules is presented and discussed [12].

[1] F.W. Bartels et al., *J. of Struc. Biol.*, **143**, 145-152, (2003).
[2] R. Eckel et al., *Biophysical Journal*, **85**, 1968-1973, (2003).
[3] A. Sischka et al., *Biophys. J*, in press (2004).
[4] R. Ros, et al., *J. of Biotechnology*, **112**, 5-12 (2004).
[5] R. Eckel et al., *Angew. Chem. Intl. Ed.*, in press (2004).
[6] A. Sischka et al. *Rev. Sci. Instrum.*, **74**, 4827-4831 (2003).
[7] A. Sischka et al., *Appl. Phys. Lett.*, submitted (2004).
[8] A. Ros et al., *J.Biotechn.*, *122*, 65-67 (2004)
[9] M. Streek et al., *J.Biotechn.*, *122*, 79-89. (2004).
[10] Eichhorn, et al., *Phys.Rev.Lett.*, *88*, 190601 (2002).
[11] Eichhorn et al., *Phys.Rev.E*, *66*, 066132 (2002).
[12] J. Roegener et al., *Anal. Chem.*, **75**, 157-159, (2003).

Fluorescence Spectroscopic Techniques to Study Protein/Protein Interactions and Conformational Changes on the Single Molecule Level

Jörg Fitter, I. Gregor and J. Enderlein
Institute of Biological Information, Processing (IBI) IBI-2:
Structural Biology, Research Center Juelich

Fluorescence spectroscopy is an experimental technique with a great potential of elucidating inter- and intramolecular interactions of biomolecules. Especially the application of fluorescence techniques to the study of single (individual) molecules has several striking advantages, if complex systems (like biological systems) with static and dynamic heterogeneity have to be investigated. This technique makes it possible to directly probe distributions of static properties as well as dynamical transitions between different states (e.g. structural conformations), without the necessity to synchronize the transitions in an ensemble. This ability becomes crucial when studying biological systems where synchronizing molecules in an ensemble is problematic due to the complex or even branched reaction pathways. Although single-molecule investigations of biological systems are still in their infancy, several promising studies in this direction have already been reported.

The fluorescent dyes used in those studies change their emission properties (e.g., emission wavelength, emission intensity, life-time, anisotropy) in accordance with changes of the direct environment of the dyes (local pH, hydrophobicity, energy transfer, etc.) during the different states of the working cycle. A more sophisticated and powerful approach for studying conformational changes on a single-molecule level as well as the interaction between different molecules provides Förster resonance energy transfer (FRET), electron transfer, and fluorescence quenching mechanisms. These techniques can be employed to study conformational changes in a time-resolved manner. An overview of these techniques and some applications will be presented.

TOWARDS SCANNING (NEAR FIELD) INFRARED LASER MICROSCOPY OF CELLS

Erik Bründermann, Andreas Bergner, Götz Wollny, Jean-Sebastien Samson and Martina Havenith-Newen
Ruhr-Universität Bochum, Physikalisch Chemie

We have developed a chemical nanoscope in the chemically important fingerprint region to monitor label free functional groups. Using our unique cw Infrared Opto Parametrc Oscillator (with output powers of 2 W) we have been able to obtain 2-dim images of cells in the spectral fingerprint bands. As a first example we present pictures of hepatocytes scanned in the range of the lipid band at 2920 cm^{-1}. The method allows a label free detection method and provides a very fast scanning method (each pixel is scanned in less than a msec). IR spectroscopy offers moreover the advantage of yielding absolute concentrations. This was demonstrated by a near infrared microscope which offers a cheap solution for the quantitative measurement of water in living cells. It is shown that IR imaging is able to monitor the influence of minimum dosages of pharmaceuticals on the intracellular water concentration on a single cell level. We were able to increase the resolution considerably when measuring in the near field limit. Using the tip of an AFM as nano-antenna we sampled the infrared spectra of the surface by the evanescent field. In a first test we achieved resolutions of 30 nm (corresponding to $\lambda/100$) in our scanning near field infrared microscope (SNIM) setup.

VOLUME, SURFACE AND STIFFNESS OF INDIVIDUAL CELLS MEASURED WITH ATOMIC FORCE MICROSCOPY

Hans Oberleithner
Institute of Physiology II, University of Muenster

Atomic force microscopy (AFM) is a tactile instrument that can be used as a nano-scope as well as a manipulative nano-tool. In principle AFM consists of a fine tip that physically scans surfaces. At low interaction forces (low pN range) the AFM tip images surfaces at sometimes molecular resolution. At high interaction forces (nN range) the AFM tip more or less strongly interacts with the surface and thus distorts it. Since forces can be controlled and measured some unique parameters as e.g. the stiffness of living cells can be quantified. We applied AFM to human endothelial cells and measured single cell volume, single cell surface and single cell stiffness in response to steroid hormones. Aldosterone, a steroid hormone known to regulate salt and water transport in kidney and to control blood pressure in humans was found to exert dramatic effects on cell volume, surface and stiffness. AFM allows the quantification of these fundamental cell characteristics. The instrument is easy to handle, commercially available and well equipped with software that supports many different applications, from molecular imaging to force-volume measurements. In conclusion, AFM is a nanotechnique with an exciting perspective in biomedical research.

Schneider SW, Matzke R, Radmacher M and Oberleithner H. Shape and volume of living aldosterone-sensitive cells imaged with the atomic force microscope. *Methods Mol Biol* 242: 255-279, 2004.

Oberleithner H, Ludwig T, Riethmuller C, Hillebrand U, Albermann L, Schafer C, Shahin V and Schillers H. Human endothelium: target for aldosterone. *Hypertension* 43: 952-956, 2004.

INDEX

D

E

F

G

H

I

T

U

V